GROWLING IN THE KENNEL OF JUSTICE

GROWLING
IN THE KENNEL
OF JUSTICE

Lawyers' reflections on the legacy
of Robert Burns

ALLAN NICOLSON

Copyright © 2014 Allan Nicolson

The moral right of the author has been asserted.

Matador
9 Priory Business Park
Kibworth Beauchamp
Leicestershire LE8 0RX, UK
Tel: (+44) 116 279 2299
Fax: (+44) 116 279 2277
Email: books@troubador.co.uk
Web: www.troubador.co.uk/matador

ISBN 978 1783064 625

British Library Cataloguing in Publication Data.
A catalogue record for this book is available from the British Library.

Typeset in Garamond by Troubador Publishing Ltd
Printed and bound in the UK by TJ International, Padstow, Cornwall

Matador is an imprint of Troubador Publishing Ltd

To my educators,
Edwin G. Macnaughton, late Rector of Hamilton Academy,
and
David M. Walker, late Regius Professor of Scots Law at the
University of Glasgow

O wad some Power the giftie gie us,
To see oursels as ithers see us!

Robert Burns, 'To a Louse', 1786

CONTENTS

CONTENTS

PREFACE

One might reasonably ask if there is any real need for yet another account of the life and times of Robert Burns and his family. Previous authors have produced works covering the entire spectrum from, at one end, lengthy dry academic studies to, at the other extreme, whimsical and sentimental journeys maintaining the myth of the ploughman poet.

My thesis is that there is a need to see Burns and his family as others saw or may have seen them. I have chosen as 'others' actual members of the legal profession who were involved in some capacity in the many skirmishes the Burns family had with the law. Their narratives are presented as a series of 'recollections' which reflect what I imagine would have been their perceptions of Robert Burns through the prism of their own views and prejudices. It will be necessary for the reader to accept that my own twenty-first century orthodoxy may have tainted what I hope to be imaginative recreations of the narrators' opinions.

I have also attempted to set Burns's life in the context of the main national and international events which occurred while he was alive – the American War of Independence, the efforts in Scotland to abolish slavery, the banking crisis which resulted in bankruptcies of many Scottish landowners, the French Revolution, the prosecutions for sedition and treason in Edinburgh and London, and the war with France. I have appended a timeline of the major events relevant to my thesis.

In some cases Burns enjoyed friendships with individual lawyers for many years: Robert Aiken, Henry Mackenzie, William Dunbar, John Syme, Alexander Cunningham and Fraser Tytler are examples. Others, such as Gavin Hamilton, John Richmond and Harry Erskine, faded out of his life after a brief association. His relationship with Robert Ainslie was the one which deteriorated most.

Most of the recollections are provided many years after the poet's death, thus leaving a reasonable time for reflection on his life. Those narrators who predeceased Burns (Sheriff William Wallace, Lord President Glenlee and Alexander Fergusson of Craigdarroch) speak just before their deaths. The chapters follow the chronological sequence of the poet's life.

Legal documents including Leases, Arbitral Findings, Wills, Assignations, Retrocessions, Writs and Defences are all included with the recollections. Most are my best efforts at deciphering originals, but in some cases I have had to use my imagination and draw on my own legal knowledge to recreate appropriate documents. I have also included a glossary of legal and other relevant terminology.

Three editions of Burns's *Poems, Chiefly in the Scottish Dialect* published in his lifetime are referred to in this work:

- the Kilmarnock Edition, published by John Wilson, Kilmarnock, in 1786
- the first Edinburgh Edition, published by William Creech, Edinburgh, in 1787
- the second Edinburgh Edition, published by William Creech, Edinburgh, in 1793

This is a work of quasi-fiction. Not everything in the recollections actually happened, but I am satisfied that everything could have happened, and that nothing is included that could not reasonably have happened. I suspect that I will infuriate many lovers of the Burns legend with these 'recollections', but in doing so, I am, for the moment only, at the end of a long queue.

Burns the poet was Scotland's greatest. Who can read 'The Twa

Dugs' or 'Ae Fond Kiss' without realising here was a man of perception and feeling with an outstanding ability to express himself? However, Burns the man was not admirable, and I hope these recollections from hard-headed men of business will together give readers a better understanding of this unhappy and tragic character.

The title of this work is taken from Burns's autobiographical letter written in 1787 to Dr John Moore, a Scottish physician and author whose novel *Zeluco* had been published in 1786. In this letter, when explaining his family history to Dr John Moore, Burns referred to the lawyers involved in his father's dispute with the landlord of the family farm as follows:

When my father died, his all went among the Hell-hounds that growl in the Kennel of Justice.

TIMELINE

1787	Burns seduces Margaret Cameron, a maidservant in Edinburgh
	Publication by William Creech of further edition of *Poems, Chiefly in the Scottish Dialect*; in this work referred to as the first Edinburgh Edition
	Death of Jean, daughter by Jean Armour
	Burns meets and forms relationship with Mrs Agnes McLehose
1788	Prison colony established at Botany Bay
	Burns seduces Jenny Clow, Mrs McLehose's maidservant
	Birth of twins by Jean Armour; they die in infancy
	Burns leases Ellisland from Patrick Miller and moves to Dumfriesshire
	He secures Excise Commission
	His marriage to Jean Armour formalised
	Birth of illegitimate son Robert Burns, by Jenny Clow
1789	Outbreak of French Revolution
	Birth of Francis-Wallace Burns
1790	Burns composes Tam o' Shanter
	Burns seduces Anna Park, barmaid at the Globe tavern Dumfries
1791	Birth of illegitimate daughter Elizabeth Park, by Anna Park
	Birth of William-Nicol Burns
	Lease of Ellisland given up
	Burns family moves to Dumfries
	He finally parts from Mrs McLehose
1792	Birth of daughter Elizabeth Riddell Burns
1793	Execution of Louis XVI
	France declares war on Great Britain
	Publication by William Creech of further edition of *Poems, Chiefly in the Scottish Dialect*; in this work referred to as the second Edinburgh Edition

1794   Birth of son James Glencairn Burns
        Treason trials in Edinburgh
1795   Burns joins Royal Dumfries Volunteers
        Death of daughter Elizabeth Riddell Burns
1796   Death of Robert Burns
        Birth of son Maxwell Burns

ACKNOWLEDGEMENTS

I owe a considerable debt of gratitude to many friends who have lived through the last three years with me in my quest to provide a new approach to analysing the life and times of Burns. Their encouragement has been inspirational, though at times it has been tinged with a vaguely amused tolerance of my enthusiasm for the project.

In particular I must thank Jean Malcolm and Martin Dawson of Edinburgh and John and Mary Robertson of Kelso for their comments on the early drafts of the manuscript. I have had great assistance from the staff at the National Library of Scotland and the librarians at the Faculty of Advocates. In relation to the Faculty Library, my researches into cases involving Burns were facilitated by the unstinting commitment of Alistair Johnson, who also read and commented on an early draft.

The cover illustration was devised by Kim McGillivray. I acknowledge with particular thanks the generosity of the Faculty of Advocates in allowing the use from their Art Collection of the images of members of Faculty who were involved with Burns's family. The line engraving, *Robert Burns, 1759–1796, Poet*, by Archibald Skirving is reproduced by the kind permission of the Scottish National Portrait Gallery.

No book should appear without the demanding scrutiny of a copy-editor, and I was fortunate to secure the services of Sarah Campbell, whose patience with me was stretched wafer thin.

In the Acknowledgement in the Second Edition of her book on Cohabitation (W. Green, 2011), my partner Kirsty Malcolm thanked me for my help and forbearance during its creation. I am happy – at last – to return the compliment.

CHAPTER 1

EARLY YEARS

1759–1780

JAMES BURNESS JUNIOR

James Burness Junior was the poet's first cousin. His father, James Burness Senior, the poet's uncle, left Kincardineshire around the same time as the poet's father William left for Edinburgh to work as a gardener. James Burness Senior settled in Montrose where, having been a successful businessman and a town councillor, he died in 1761 leaving James Junior at a tender eleven years of age.

James Burness Junior became a solicitor. He corresponded with Burns throughout his life and finally met him in Stonehaven in 1787. He died in 1837.

My name is James Burness. I am a lawyer in practice in Montrose. I am fifty-six years of age. I make this statement on 31st March 1806.

I am a first cousin of the late Robert Burns. My father (who was also called James) and the poet's father William were brothers. They were brought up in Kincardineshire. My grandfather, Robert Burnes, was the tenant of a farm at Clochanhill in Dunottar parish. He had a large family.

My father was the eldest surviving son and might have been expected to continue with farming, but I think that, even as a young man, he had a vision that urban business would offer a more secure life than being a tenant farmer, so he moved to Montrose and became a successful merchant. That was after my grandfather had moved from Clochanhill to a smaller farm at Falside in Kineff in 1745, and around the time he retired from farming altogether in about 1747. My grandfather's record in farming was not one of success, and, sadly, the same has been true of succeeding generations.

With the demise of the Burnes farming enterprise in Kincardineshire, my uncles Robert and William had to find other employment. Uncle Robert sought work in England, and Uncle William secured a post as a gardener in Edinburgh after which he moved to Ayrshire, settling eventually in Maybole where in about 1756 he purchased a cottage and smallholding of just over seven acres which he intended to establish as a market garden. In addition, at this time my Uncle William did contract gardening work. He married my aunt Agnes in 1757, and my cousin Robert, the poet, was born on 25th January 1759. Another son, my cousin Gilbert, was born the following year.

My father died in 1761 when I was eleven years old. Uncle William and I corresponded thereafter, so I was aware of the growing number of my cousins in Ayrshire.

I learned a lot about my cousin's early life when I met him in 1787. He reminisced a great deal about Ayrshire and although he was living in Edinburgh by then, being feted as a celebrity and very comfortable financially, I got the impression he hankered after a simple country life while at the same time envying the sure and steady income I had as a lawyer in a large town.

Throughout his life Robert seemed to be full of contradictions. For example, he quizzed me relentlessly about anything I had learned from my father about our family history. He seemed obsessed with the idea that our grandfather had taken up arms in the 1715 rebellion in the Stuart cause, and that he had suffered financially as a result of his support of Jacobitism. I told him neither I nor my mother knew anything of this, and that my father would surely have mentioned it if it were true. I suspected that the failure of our grandfather's business was more due to poor harvests. It was as if Robert was wishing the Jacobite connection to be true. He certainly seemed to be a patriotic Scot. I can well believe that, as he put it in his autobiographical letter[1] of 2nd August 1787 to Doctor John Moore, the story of William Wallace "poured a Scottish prejudice in my veins, which will boil along there till the flood-gates of life shut in eternal rest".

The education Robert received can at best be described as piecemeal. Our government has legislated for a system whereby a school is to be established in every parish, financed at the expense of landowners and administered by the local Kirk Session, whose responsibility it is to appoint the schoolmaster. No such school seemed to have existed in Alloway, so Robert's education was a rather informal affair. He and Gilbert received a little structured education at the hands of, firstly, William Campbell, at Alloway Mill, and then John Murdoch, a young man who was engaged by my uncle and four other local families to educate their children at a small building in the

4

vicinity. This was on the basis that Murdoch, then only eighteen years of age, would board with each family in turn. This boarding arrangement terminated in May 1766 when my uncle and his family moved from the cottage and smallholding in Alloway to Mount Oliphant, the farm of about seventy acres where my uncle took on his first tenancy at an annual rent of £40. By the time of the move to Mount Oliphant the family had increased to four with the arrivals of my cousins Agnes and Annabella. My uncle was unable to find a purchaser for the Alloway property so he had to borrow from his landlord at Mount Oliphant to enable him to stock the farm, and he used the Alloway property as security for these loans. He eventually sold the Alloway property in 1781 for £160.

Robert and Gilbert's attendance at Murdoch's little school during the next two years was less regular, and in 1768, following some changes, the young teacher obtained a post in Dumfries. This caused an interruption to the boys' formal education, as Mount Oliphant was somewhat isolated and so beyond the reach of most tutors, and in any case, their labours were needed on the farm. Apparently my uncle made every effort to continue his family's education himself. He was a subscriber to the Ayr library, which prompted literary discussions after the work of the day was done.

After Murdoch returned to Ayr in 1772, having been appointed English master in the burgh school, he visited my uncle and persuaded him to send Robert and Gilbert week about to the parish school of Dalrymple for the summer term to improve their writing. The following year Robert was sent to Murdoch's school in Ayr for a week to improve his grasp of English, in the hope that he would be able to tutor his brother and sisters. By now my cousins William, John and Isabella had been born, so there could be a veritable classroom at Mount Oliphant. After school in Ayr Robert then had to return home to help with the harvest, but he was allowed a further two weeks with Murdoch when the harvest was over, and at that time he learned some French and Latin.

When Robert was sixteen he was sent to a school in Kirkoswald over the late summer to learn the elements of surveying. Thereafter he was simply self-taught, as his days were taken up with arduous work on the farms, firstly at Mount Oliphant and then at Lochlie, where the family moved in 1777 after the termination of the Mount Oliphant lease. According to Robert, taking on the lease at Lochlie would prove to be a fatal mistake on the part of my Uncle William due to the stress and anxiety caused by the litigation that was to ensue over it. I think this was an exaggeration by my cousin. My father died when he was only forty-four, Uncle Robert when he was seventy and Uncle William when he was sixty-three. One can hardly say Uncle William had a premature death, bearing in mind his years of manual labour.

Robert maintained he owed a huge debt of gratitude to John Murdoch, who is clearly of a liberal persuasion. Robert praised Murdoch for introducing him to literary culture through, in particular, Arthur Masson's *A Collection of English Prose and Verse, For the Use of Schools* which they studied and discussed together. Many of Robert's ideas were derived from the works in that book and the liberal philosophy which underpins them.

Uncle William was a litigious character. It is well known that towards the end of his life he was involved in a protracted and very bitter arbitration and court case with his landlord at Lochlie, the Ayr merchant David McClure. What is not so widely appreciated is that my uncle was himself a landlord in respect of his smallholding in Alloway, which he let out over the years, and in 1779 he commenced legal proceedings against Joseph Norman, a Seedsman in Ayr, who had become my uncle's tenant of about four acres in August 1777. I believe Joseph Norman was the elected Master Freemason at Lodge

St David where Robert was entered an apprentice and passed and raised in 1781.

The dispute between my uncle and Norman was referred to arbitration by two arbiters, jointly appointed. On 8th November 1781, a Decreet Arbitral[2] was issued in favour of my uncle in respect of his rent and expenses. The remarkable feature of these proceedings was that one of the arbiters who decided the case for Uncle William was none other than his then landlord the aforementioned David McClure! I can only assume that McClure had been nominated by Norman, and my uncle had nominated John McKenzie, the other arbiter.

Later

There has been some confusion about the spelling of our family surname. My grandfather's surname was Burnes but my father decided to use Burness, which I have adopted. Robert's father continued to use Burnes after he moved to Ayrshire, as did Robert from time to time until about 1786 after which he consistently used Burns.

As stated above, I met Robert by arrangement in Stonehaven in 1787 and we corresponded from time to time, although I never visited him at Ellisland or in Dumfries. He wrote to me in February 1789 to let me know that he had obtained his commission as an excise officer, as an optional career to follow if farming proved to be unsuccessful. Shortly before his death, claiming to be in distressed circumstances, he appealed to me for a loan of £10, which I immediately sent. He did not survive to encash the note.

After Robert's death I wrote to his widow offering to bring up one of her sons, but she replied that 'the gentlemen who had so much interested themselves for the family did not wish that she come to any resolution with respect to parting with any of the boys'. She was referring to Doctor William Maxwell and John Syme, who were doing what they could to support the family. Her inclination was to keep all her children with her, as they would be a comfort to her, and that was the decision she finally made.

CHAPTER 2

A RUN ON THE BANK

1780

SIR ADAM FERGUSSON OF KILKERRAN

Sir Adam Fergusson was the Third Baronet of Kilkerran. He was the son of Sir James Fergusson of Kilkerran, Lord Kilkerran, one of the Senators of the College of Justice.

He was a graduate of the University of Edinburgh and was admitted to the Faculty of Advocates in 1755. He served as Clerk of Faculty.

Fergusson was Member of Parliament for both Ayrshire and for Edinburgh at different times between 1774 and 1796. He voted against the abolition of the slave trade in 1796.

He was one of the partners in the failed Douglas Heron Bank. He subscribed to the first Edinburgh Edition of Burns's *Poems, Chiefly in the Scottish Dialect.*

Although Fergusson was described by James Boswell as "A vile Whig",[1] he was a great friend of Henry Dundas, the high Tory who became Viscount Melville. Sir Adam Fergusson died in 1813.

My name is Adam Fergusson. I am an advocate and landowner. I am seventy-three years of age. I make this statement on 31st October 1806.

Robert Burns and I enjoyed a mutual respect. In 'The Author's Earnest Cry and Prayer', he described me as "aith detestin' chaste Kilkerran". I was flattered.

I knew William Burnes, the poet's father, as my country estate, Kilkerran, lies not many miles distant from where he started his market garden in Alloway and his first farming business at Mount Oliphant. I am sorry to say that William Burnes chose a singularly inauspicious time to start his farming venture in 1765.

Around this time the economy of the County of Ayr started to undergo a change. Having been buoyant, with the manufacture of silk and carpet weaving predominant, a recession was starting to take effect. Those involved in agriculture were struggling to make ends meet, with prices for their produce being barely sufficient to cover costs. These problems were compounded as a result of the failure of a local bank.

A new bank had been established in Ayr in 1769. It traded as The Ayr Bank, but its proper legal name was Douglas Heron & Company. It expanded rapidly, with branches being opened in various towns in Scotland. It was actually a partnership, and the liability of each of the shareholders, or partners, was not limited. If the bank failed, the personal assets of the partners would be called on to meet any deficit.

The original partners were from the top tier of Scottish society, but the board of directors, of which I was a member, contained no-one with any experience of banking.

Within a very short time, the Douglas Heron Bank had overextended itself by giving excessive loans to privileged customers – in many cases to the partners themselves – and had sought to conceal the perilous position it was in simply by borrowing more from external sources. This overtrading coincided with the insolvency of the London banking house of Neale, James, Fordyce and Doune in 1772, with the result that banks generally became more hesitant to make loans to one another, and by 1773 they were refusing the Douglas Heron Bank any credit at all. In August of that year the partners met and decided to wind up the partnership, as there was clearly a deficit. In fact the losses were astronomic, and the partners were fearful that they might be obliged to pay in more than the amount of working capital for which they were liable under the partnership agreement.

As well as being a director, I myself was one of the partners, but happily I was able to meet my obligations. However, when those charged with winding up the affairs of the Douglas Heron Bank attempted to recover the large sums owed by several partners, bankruptcies ensued. The whole affair became a dreadful embarrassment to me personally. It demonstrated the wisdom of separating one's business from one's legal practice. In one case, my brother-in-law David Dalrymple, Lord Hailes, proposed to recuse himself (i.e. stand down) as the judge in a case brought by the Douglas Heron Bank against Baron Grant, a debtor of the Bank. He claimed that he was conflicted because I was a partner in, and therefore also in effect a debtor of, the Bank, but the court held that he could not decline to hear the case as there were over two hundred partners and most of the judiciary were related to them to some degree!

Two other cases illustrate how the liquidation of the Douglas Heron Bank became a plentiful source of work or 'dripping roast' for the legal profession. Captain John Blair was an original partner who held two shares of £500 each, of which £775 had been paid up. Captain Blair died in October 1772, just as the problems with the Douglas Heron Bank were becoming apparent. Article seventeen of the partnership agreement for the Bank had provided that:[2]

in the event of the death or insolvency of any of the partners, the heir, executor or assigns of the deceast, and the creditors of the insolvent partner, shall be obliged to receive and draw their share in the stock and profits thereof, as the same shall stand at the last preceding settlement of the company's affairs, with interest thereon at 4 per cent from that settlement until payment is demanded, and the legal interest thereof afterward till complete payment.

David Blair had been appointed as his late brother's executor, and brought an action against the Bank for payment of the value of the two shares and the profit due on them as at November 1771, the last date of settlement prior to the date of death. This was in the hope of avoiding the loss which every partner in the Bank would sustain from its total bankruptcy. David Blair's case was argued by Robert Macqueen and Robert Blair. The Bank's administrators were represented by Ilay Campbell and Alexander Murray. An impressive debate ensued, as reflected in the fact that all these advocates later became distinguished judges including Lords President (Ilay Campbell and Robert Blair), Lord Justice Clerk (Robert Macqueen) and Lord Henderland (Alexander Murray). The Court determined that as the Bank had become totally insolvent between November 1771 and October 1772, David Blair could not recover the apparent value of his late brother's shares. He appealed to the House of Lords, but was unsuccessful.

As mentioned previously, in August 1773 the partners had passed a resolution[3] that:

from and after that date, the Company shall give over the business of banking in all its branches.

At subsequent meetings in 1776, it having become clear that the Bank had incurred a loss of £70,000 over and above the subscribed capital, it was resolved that all partners should pay up not only any unpaid original capital but also a further sum of £200 on each £500 share.

An action was brought by the Bank's administrators against Alexander Hair and his trustees, in whom his estate was vested. The defenders did not object to paying up the capital, but were refusing the call for the additional contribution of £200 on Hair's original £500 share.

Clause 19 of the partnership agreement[4] had provided that:

> nothing herein contained shall be understood to import a power in any general meeting whatever to compel any partner to pay or contribute anything more to the company-stock than the precise sum by him originally subscribed for.

Once again the Bank's administrators were represented by Ilay Campbell. The advocate for Hair and his Trustees was David Rae (later Lord Eskgrove). Rae argued that the Clause meant that the meeting had no right to compel a contribution of this kind, but the Court found that the additional payment had to be made.

It might have seemed a little far-fetched to imagine that the plight of the partners in the Douglas Heron Bank would have an impact on the poet's father. But around the time of the judgment in the Hair case (July 1778), William Burnes moved to become the tenant of Lochlie Farm near Tarbolton having given up Mount Oliphant in 1777 on the expiry of his lease. He became the tenant of an Ayr merchant called David McClure, a gentleman known to me as another partner in the Douglas Heron Bank. The fortunes of the Burns family were about to become enmeshed in what would transpire to be a web of financial manipulation and mismanagement.

CHAPTER 3

PARTNERSHIP

1781–1782

ROBERT AIKEN

Robert Aiken, born in 1739, was the son of a master mariner. He became a lawyer in Ayr with a diverse practice. Aiken, known as 'Orator Bob', was involved with Robert Burns and his family on a wide variety of issues, though his main claim to fame was as Burns's first patron.

Aiken collected about one quarter of the subscriptions for the Kilmarnock Edition and tried, without success, to find him a publisher for a second edition. Aiken and Burns continued to correspond after Burns left Ayrshire. Burns dedicated 'The Cotter's Saturday Night' to Aiken.

Aiken was a Freemason whose Mother Lodge was Lodge Leith Kilwinning.

He died in 1807.

My name is Robert Aiken. I am a lawyer. I am sixty-seven years of age. I make this statement on 31st March 1806. In 1781 Robert Burns and his family resided at Lochlie Farm, a farm extending to about 130 acres of mixed quality, which lies about three miles north-west of Mauchline. The received wisdom at the time was that a farm needed to extend to at least 160 acres to be economic, so it was not surprising that the Burns family survived at just above subsistence level.

Robert combined the heavy work of farming as his father's labourer with the lighter side of socialising. The village of Tarbolton is about five miles west of Mauchline, and Robert and his brother Gilbert were leading figures in the Tarbolton Bachelors' Club, a debating society which had been formed at the end of 1780 by Robert, Gilbert and five other local lads to discuss philosophical issues. Membership was restricted to bachelors who belonged to the Parish of Tarbolton, although men who later married could continue if a majority of the members agreed. By 1781, the Club had expanded by admission of five more members. One of the Rules of the Club,[1] prepared by Robert, indicates the types who he felt should be drawn to the Club, and the outlook Robert had on life at the time:

> Every man proper for a member of this society must have a frank, honest, open heart; above anything dirty or mean; and must be a professed lover of one or more of the female sex. No haughty, self-conceited person, who looks upon himself as superior to the rest of the club, and especially no mean-spirited, worldly mortal, whose only will is to heap up money, shall upon any pretence whatever be admitted. In short, the proper person for this society is a cheerful, honest-hearted lad, who, if he has a friend that is true, and a mistress that

is kind, and as much wealth as genteelly to make both
ends meet – is just as happy as this world can make him.

A great deal of nonsense has been written about Robert's
humble background and supposed lack of education. In refutation
of that I set out two of the issues debated at the Club: "whether is
the savage man or the peasant of a civilised country in the most
happy situation"; and "whether do we derive more happiness from
love or friendship". These are classic debating points.

Robert was twenty-two years of age. He had been working with
his father on the farm for more than four years, and he was bored
by the monotony and repetitive nature of the work. He craved the
excitement of living in town rather than on a remote farm. He felt
that his father had been a bit devious, having told him that he
needed his support as he could not afford to employ staff. In any
event, his brother Gilbert was only a year younger than him, and
Gilbert had always seen his future in farming. There had also been
problems at the farm, in that his father was in dispute with his
landlord over who should bear the costs of carrying out
improvements.

William Burnes was of a rather tetchy nature. In many ways he
could be described as a typical farmer, self-centred and inward
looking. He kept his opinions to himself, and he certainly did not
approve of Robert and Gilbert expressing theirs at their debating
Club. He also felt that Robert spent too much time writing poetry
and going out socialising.

For some time Gilbert and Robert had been raising flax and
selling it. They had won an award for the quality of the flax they
produced. One of their buyers, Alexander Peacock, had a flax-
dressing business in the Glasgow Vennel in Irvine. I think Peacock
was Robert's mother's half-brother. In any event, Robert and he got

talking, and the upshot was Peacock offered Robert a partnership in the business.

Around this time Robert expressed an interest in Freemasonry. My local lodge is Lodge Ayr Kilwinning and in 1781 I was well aware of what was happening in Tarbolton. Some of the members of Lodge Tarbolton Kilwinning had applied in 1773 to form another Lodge, under the jurisdiction of the Grand Lodge of Scotland, and Lodge St David Tarbolton had been chartered. The remaining members of the original Lodge had then arranged for Lodge St James to be chartered in 1778. This unusual state of affairs – two Lodges in one village – was soon seen to be a costly way to arrange Masonic matters, and on 25th June 1781 a union was effected under the name and charter of Lodge St David. Robert was initiated into the amalgamated Lodge on 4th July.

Robert sought advice from brother Freemasons about the advisability of going into partnership with Peacock. He was told he would need to see the business accounts, have a written Contract of Co-Partnery setting out how long the partnership would last, how the profits were to be shared and how the firm would be wound up if they fell out or something happened to one of the partners. Robert chose to ignore this advice, and he and Peacock went on to trade on the basis of a verbal agreement.

To be honest, I have no idea what drove Robert to move to Irvine. At the time he must have been desperate to get away from the farm. Flax dressing is a disgusting process, and Robert must have been aware of that, for he had been selling flax to dressers. The rotting of the flax and the beating of the rotted material to separate out the useful fibres results in a noxious smell and the subsequent heckling (drawing the flax through combs of nails) was physically exhausting for Robert, who was working even longer hours than on the farm. I am sure the dust produced in the process got into his lungs and contributed to his later illnesses.

By 1st October, when Robert was passed and raised as a Freemason at Lodge St David, his view on life in town had changed; he seemed much less keen than before on turning his back on farming. Gilbert later said that Robert was much more suited to work in the open air, as being inside all day made him ill and depressed, and that Robert had written to his father to this effect on 27th December 1781. An excerpt from the letter reads:[2]

> Honoured Sir,
>
> I have purposely delayed writing, in the hope that I should have the pleasure of seeing you, on New-year's day; but work comes so hard upon us that I do not choose to be absent on that account, as well as for some other little reasons, which I shall tell you at meeting …
>
> Irvine. 27th December 1781   Robert Burness

It transpired that the flax-dressing partnership was, as Robert described it, 'a sadly unlucky affair'. Not only was Robert's constitution not up to the work involved, but in addition, Peacock proved to be a scoundrel of the first water who consistently stole from the firm. And to cap it all, while he and Robert were out on Hogmanay giving the New Year a welcoming carousal, Peacock's wife, apparently in a drunken stupor herself, contrived to set the premises alight. So they now had no premises, no stock and no money, although at least they did not owe anything to creditors. So that was the end of flax dressing for Robert. He returned to Lochlie early in 1782.

Later

The amalgamation of the two Tarbolton Masonic Lodges was not a success. On 17th June 1782, some members seceded and re-formed a Lodge with the name Lodge St James Tarbolton. Robert was appointed Depute Master of that Lodge on 27th July 1784.

I acted on behalf of Robert's friend Gavin Hamilton in his long-running disputes with Mauchline Kirk Session, and Robert rewarded me with a complimentary mention in 'Holy Willie's Prayer'.

I supported Robert in promoting the publication of the Kilmarnock Edition and made enquiries of some Edinburgh contacts about a second edition after John Wilson turned down Robert's proposal; these came to naught, but when Robert finally made his own deal with William Creech, I subscribed to the Edinburgh Edition.

Robert and I kept in touch throughout his lifetime. By way of example, he wrote to me from Dumfries on 16th July 1793 on behalf of our mutual friend Mrs Muir of Tarbolton Mill, who was likely to be involved in difficulties over a Will. In his letter, Robert advised that a friend of his, Robert Ainslie, Writer to the Signet, would take on her case pro bono, and that our fellow Ayrshireman, David Cathcart, would advocate the case at small expense.

I was one of the nine admirers of Robert who attended the first dinner in honour of his memory in the summer of 1801. John Ballantine, Provost of Ayr, organised the convention, those attending at his invitation with me being William Crawford of Doonside, Patrick Douglas of Garallan, Primrose Kennedy of Drumellan, Hew Ferguson and David Scott from Ayr, Professor Thomas Jackson from St Andrews and the Reverend Hamilton Paul. We had an enjoyable evening of reminiscences, and resolved that the dinner should be an annual occasion, to take place on 29th January, which we supposed at the time to have been Robert's birth date. These annual dinners continue to this day, and although we now know that Robert's birth date was 25th January, we have judged it expedient to hold the dinner once more in the summer months.

CHAPTER 4

LOCHLIE FARM

1783

SHERIFF WILLIAM WALLACE OF CAIRNHILL

William Wallace was the son of Robert Wallace, Writer to the
Signet. He was admitted to the Faculty of Advocates on 15th
February 1752. He succeeded Sir Adam Fergusson of Kilkerran
as Clerk of Faculty in 1758.

He was appointed Professor of Universal History in 1755 and
Professor of Scots Law in 1765, both tenures at the
University of Edinburgh.

William Wallace served as Sheriff at Ayr from 1775 until his
death on 28th December 1786.

My name – a famous one which I have found to be a burden – is William Wallace. I make this statement on 31st March 1786.

I am a great admirer of Robert Burns. I consider him to be a gifted poet. I have known him for about five years, since his induction as a Freemason into Lodge St David at Tarbolton in 1781.

As the local Sheriff at Ayr I have an insight into the business affairs of the locals, and being a Freemason sometimes enables me to glean additional background information on disputes. This is helpful to me, although, of course, it does not have any impact on the decisions I am called upon to make, which must be based solely on the evidence presented to me.

The Sheriff Clerk in a small court such as Ayr is also always a good source of background material when a new dispute comes to court. It was therefore useful to me to learn from him what the local gossip was when, in May 1783, I was presented with a Petition for the sequestration of the assets of William Burnes, Robert's father.

According to information gleaned by my clerk at the local market, William Burnes had taken on the tenancy of Lochlie, a farm of about 130 acres near Tarbolton, which was owned – or so it appeared at the time – by David McClure of Shawwood, an Ayr businessman. McClure and Burnes had verbally agreed a lease of the farm for thirty-eight years at an annual rent of £130. McClure had undertaken to make extensive improvements to Lochlie including renovation of the steading, enclosing some fields within walls, liming fields and draining a loch.

Verbal leases almost inevitably give rise to misunderstandings and disputes, and apparently there was a long-running argument about whether Burnes was entitled to set off the cost of some works he had carried out on the farm against rents due by him. This had initially been conducted between Burnes and McClure's factor, and I have often wondered if these discussions and the steps later taken by McClure are reflected in the verse Robert included in 'The Twa Dugs':[1]

> I've notic'd, on our laird's court-day, –
> An' mony a time my heart's been wae, –
> Poor tenant bodies, scant o' cash,
> How they maun thole a factor's snash;
> He'll stamp an' threaten, curse an' swear
> He'll apprehend them, poind their gear;
> While they maun stan', wi' aspect humble,
> An' hear it a', an' fear an' tremble!

In any event, negotiations with the factor were going nowhere and in September 1782, Burnes and McClure himself met at Simson's Inn, Ayr, to try to resolve their differences. Both were strong willed, and neither would give way. They decided to refer the dispute to arbitration, and appointed James Grieve of Boghead and Charles Norval, the gardener at Coilsfield, as arbiters.

The arbiters held a series of hearings taking evidence, but unfortunately they were unable to agree, so they appointed an oversman to break the deadlock. John Hamilton of Sundrum agreed to act as the oversman. This was about a month before the matter came before me. As it happens, Hamilton is a brother Freemason.

McClure had clearly run out of patience and decided to pre-empt the outcome of the arbitration by seeking Burnes's sequestration. The Petition[2] was in the following terms:

UNTO THE SHERIFF OF THE COUNTY OF AIR
PETITION
of

DAVID McCLURE, Merchant in Air,

PETITIONER

for

Sequestration of WILLIAM BURNS, farmer in Lochlie.

HUMBLY SHEWETH:-

(One)   That William Burns in Lochlie is possessed of that farm, part of the Barony of Halfmark in the Parish of Tarbolton, and has done so for five years preceding Martinmas last, at the rent of One hundred and thirty pounds Sterling yearly by set from the Petitioner, and is presently owing upwards of Five hundred pounds Sterling besides the current year's rent;

(Two)   That the said William Burns, having upon frivolous pretences refused payment of the rent, his claims of retention came at last to be submitted to arbiters and then laid before Mr Hamilton of Sundrum as oversman, to determine upon them, but as there was no written tack or minute of bargain between the Petitioner and the said William Burns, it is informed that he is immediately to quit the possession, and is preparing himself accordingly by dispossession of his stock and crops, to disappoint the Petitioner of his fund of payment, which obliges him to make application.

                   MAY IT THEREFORE please your Lordship to order that Petition be served upon the said William Burns, and him to lodge his Answers thereto in a short space, and in the meantime to grant warrant for sequestrating the whole stock and crops in the barn and barnyard upon said lands, all to remain till payment is made of the bygone rent, at least till sufficient caution is found for what may be due, and likeways of the current year's rent.

According to Justice, &c.

The Petition was in order (apart from the spelling of Burnes's surname) and as a prima facie case was made out, I ordained that Burnes be served with a full copy of the Petition and of my deliverance thereon, and that he should lodge his Answers thereto in the Sheriff Clerk's office at Ayr within four days after he should be so served with Certification, and in the meantime I granted warrant to sheriff officers to sequestrate and secure the stock and crop in the barn and barnyard, but only for payment of the current year's rent.

James Gordon, one of the sheriff officers, subsequently reported to the court and certified that he had served the Petition on Burnes personally, requiring him to lodge his Answers thereto in the Sheriff Clerk's office at Ayr, and had sequestrated and secured four horses, two mares, thirteen cows, two calves, one ewe, two lambs, various cut crops and farm implements – all to remain under sure sequestration for payment of the current year's rent when due.

Burnes lodged Answers to the Petition[3] which made his position clear:

UNTO THE SHERIFF OF THE COUNTY OF AIR
ANSWERS for WILLIAM BURNS, farmer in Lochlie
to the Petition
of
David McClure, Merchant in Air,
for
Sequestration of William Burns

(One)   Admitted that the Respondent is possessed of said farm for five years preceding Martinmas last at a rent of One hundred and thirty pounds sterling yearly by let from the Petitioner. *Quoad ultra* denied. Explained and averred that there was an agreement that the Petitioner would carry out extensive works on said farm which the Petitioner has failed to do. The Respondent has carried out said works and has ploughed and sowed part of the Lands. The rents to Martinmas last are already paid by reason of compensation due to the Respondent in respect of the said work carried out by him which was a liability of the Petitioner. The questions between the Petitioner and the Respondent as to the period to Martinmas last are the subject of the arbitration process referred to by the Petitioner. On completion of said process the Respondent will pay whatever is found to be due to the Petitioner. The action is accordingly premature. The award of sequestration should be recalled.

(Two)   Denied.

PLEAS-IN-LAW

(One)   The Petitioner's averments being irrelevant *et separatim* lacking in specification, the Petition should be dismissed.

(Two)   The Petitioner's averments, so far as material, being unfounded in fact, decree of absolvitor should be pronounced.

(Three)   There being no circumstances to justify the award of sequestration, no such award should be made.

IN RESPECT WHEREOF

On the calling date I was advised that McClure had given an undertaking not to seek to sell anything attached by the sequestration meantime, and on that basis Burnes would not take any steps to insist on his motion for recall of the sequestration. McClure's lawyer then lodged Replies[4] to his pleadings in the following terms:

UNTO THE SHERIFF OF THE COUNTY OF AIR
REPLIES
for
DAVID McCLURE, Merchant in Air,
to
the Answers of William Burns in Lochlie

The Petitioner denies there was any missive of agreement respecting the let of the Lands of Lochlie to the Respondent as he alleges. But he affirms that the rent of said Lands was as set forth in the Petition. Sometime ago the Respondent made out an Account in his own hand writing which he called an Account of Charge and Discharge betwixt him and the Petitioner, in which Account he himself states the rent in the same manner as set forth in the Petition. This Account with other papers is lying before the Arbiter, Mr Hamilton of Sundrum. The Petitioner allows that the Respondent has ploughed and sowed part of the Lands, but whether so much as ought to have been done he cannot say; but he submits to your Lordship whether thirteen black cattle (which by the Execution of Sequestration herewith produced, your Lordship will see is all the Respondent has on the farm) be an adequate number for a farm of the extent and that pays the rent which the Respondent's farm does. It will no doubt appear to your Lordship that there ought to have been at least double that quantity, but few as they are, and notwithstanding your Lordship's sequestration, the Petitioner is well informed that since your Lordship's warrant was execute the Respondent has actually carried off and sold part of that number at a public market.

As the Respondent acknowledges the possession, it cannot be understood that he should possess these lands without paying rent, but he does not so much as pretend to say that he has any receipts or discharges to show that he has paid the rent up to any given period during his possession. Therefore his saying that the rents are paid up till Martinmas last is a mere allegation without the smallest foundation. It is therefore humbly hoped from these causes your Lordship will see no cause to alter or recall your Warrant of Sequestration as craved.

David McClure

The case was in effect sisted pending the determination by Mr Hamilton, the oversman in the arbitration. His decision was issued three months later, and its terms were incorporated in the Decree Arbitral.[5]

In short, and in round terms, the oversman decided that Burnes was due to pay £775, being rent of £715 and £60 in refund of improvements. Against that, Burnes was found to be entitled to various allowances for the improvements he had carried out. These totalled £543 so the net sum due to McClure was reduced to £232.

McClure registered the Decree Arbitral in the Sheriff Court making it legally enforceable, and enabling him to serve a charge on Burnes.

The resolution of the dispute was then taken out of my hands. It transpired that McClure was in dispute with John McAdam of Craigengillan who had a mortgage over Lochlie. I was aware that McAdam had loaned substantial sums to various partners in the Douglas Heron Bank, and where he had mortgages over the debtors' properties, he was seeking to recover what was due to him by calling up his securities. It was common knowledge that McClure was heavily in debt due to the failure of the Bank, where he was a partner, and he had borrowed substantial sums from McAdam. As it was pointless for McAdam to sue McClure in view of his embarrassed financial position, he had brought court actions against tenants of McClure in order that, pending him taking over the properties or selling them, the tenants should pay their rents direct to him as the mortgage holder.

In view of this, Burnes was advised to seek a Suspension of the Decree against him to postpone the operation of the procedure to follow the Decree Arbitral pending a further hearing. That Bill of Suspension had to be raised in the Court of Session in Edinburgh. That Court is the forum where cases of particular importance can be initiated, but it also reviews decisions of lower courts, including the Sheriff Court. To understand how matters developed in the Burnes case, it will be useful to know how matters proceed in the Court of Session.

This Court comprises a Lord President and fourteen other Senators of the College of Justice. They sit as a body only in the most complex cases; for ordinary business the quorum is nine. They make their decisions largely on the basis of written submissions from advocates. However, most cases are initiated in what is known as the 'Outer House', where a single Senator, known as a Lord Ordinary, hears various applications and straightforward processes. Some he may deal with himself and others he may report to what is known as the 'Inner House' for a determination.

A Bill of Suspension[6] in the following terms was duly lodged:

UNTO THE RIGHT HONOURABLE
THE LORDS OF COUNCIL AND SESSION

PETITION
of
WILLIAM BURNS, in Lochlee
for
LETTERS OF SUSPENSION

HUMBLY SHEWETH:-

> My Lords of Council and Session Unto your Lordships means and shows William Burns in Lochlee That I am lately charged by virtue of the Sheriff of Air his Decreet to make payment to David McLure of Shawood, Merchant in Air, of the Sum of Two hundred and thirty one pounds Sterling, being a Ballance of rent due by me at Martinmas MDCC and eighty one, Conform to Decreet Arbitral pronounced by John Hamilton of Sundrum, Esquire, on a Submission betwixt the said David McLure and me and that within a certain Short Space under the pain of poinding &c. most wrongously and unjustly Considering That John McAdam of Craigengillan, Esquire, as having an Heritable Security over the Lands for which the Rents Charged for is due for Eight thousand pounds Sterling, lately brought an action against me and the other Tenants of said Lands for payment of the Rents due by us, And therefore I am not in safety to pay the Sums Charged for to the Charger without Mr

McAdam's Consent, And therefore the foresaid Charge ought to be Simpliciter Suspended nevertheless for the more obedience I am willing to find Caution in common form.

THEREFORE, I beseech your Lordships for Letters of Suspension of the foresaid Charge upon Caution.

According to Justice &c.

This Bill was heard by Lord Swinton in the Outer House on 25th August 1783 and he refused to grant it because Burnes had not given specific details of the case allegedly brought against him by McAdam of Craigengillan, nor had he disclosed the name of the court where the alleged action had been brought, nor had he raised any Multiplepoinding.

I do not think that Burnes was well advised to proceed as he did. It seemed clear to me that the matter would have been resolved there and then by a Multiplepoinding, whereby Burnes would have deposited the sum due by him in Court, after which it would have been for the Court to intimate this to all possible claimants and, after hearing their claims, to decide who was entitled to it. Burnes would have obtained a Discharge of his liability from the Court and there would have been no possibility of his having to pay the sum due twice.

Extraneous events then impacted on the dispute between Burnes and McClure. The administrator of the Douglas Heron Bank was pursuing McClure for his cash contribution to the Bank's deficit, and McClure was bankrupted. Burnes was now advised to take up Lord Swinton's suggestion of initiating a Multiplepoinding. Robert Blair, advocate, was instructed. He was very familiar with the plight of partners in the Douglas Heron Bank as he had been involved in many previous cases involving the Bank's administrator. Having examined the title deeds of Lochlie, he concluded that McClure was only a joint owner of the farm along with John Campbell of Wellwood and George McCree of Pitcon, as the three had purchased various properties, including Lochlie, in joint names about ten years earlier. It was a mystery why Campbell and McCree (who were also now bankrupt) had not been involved in the prior litigation, but as they were joint owners it was necessary that they be included in the Multiplepoinding for their interests. An action[7] was raised in the following terms:

> GEORGE By the Grace of God King of Great Britain France and Ireland, defender of the Faith
>
> To
>
> Messengers at arms our Sheriffs in that part greeting Whereas it is humbly meant and shown to us by WILLIAM BURNS, in Lochlie, the pursuer, Mentioning that where the pursuer is daily charged, troubled, molested and pursued by JOHN McCULLOCH, Merchant in Ayr, DAVID EWEN, Merchant there, JAS. HUME, Writer there, DOUGLAS, HERON & Co., late Bankers there, and GEORGE HOME OF BRANXTON, their factor and manager, JOHN CAMPBELL of WELLWOOD, DAVID McCLURE of SHAWWOOD, and GEORGE McCREE of PITCON, the defenders, for payment making to them of the rents due by the pursuer for the said farm of Lochlie belonging in joint property to the said Messers John Campbell, David McClure and George McCree, most wrongously, Considering that the pursuer can only be liable in once

and single payment of the rents of the said farm and that to the person or persons who shall be found by the Lords of Council and Session to have best right thereto, And therefore the said John McCulloch, David Ewen and Jas. Hume, Douglas Heron & Co. and their said factor and manager, John Campbell, David McClure and George McCree, ought and should exhibit and produce before the said Lords the several rights and grounds of debt by which they claim right to the foresaid rents and should discuss the same before the said Lords, to the end that the party having the best right thereto may be preferred to the said rents after deduction and allowance to the pursuer of the expense of this process, And the remanent persons should be by Decreet foresaid discharged from further molesting and pursuing the said pursuer thereafter in time coming conform to the Laws and daily practice of this Realm used and observed in similar cases as is alleged.

According to Justice &c.

Lord Braxfield heard the case in the Outer House and decided that the administrator of the Douglas Heron Bank was entitled to the sum William Burnes had lodged and the further year's rent which had fallen due; so McClure himself received nothing.

Robert Burns's delight at the outcome of McClure's claim was short-lived. The dispute had taken two years to resolve, and it had taken its toll on his father. On 13th February 1784, three weeks after Lord Braxfield's decision, William Burnes died. I believe his estate, such as it was, passed to his widow and children.

CHAPTER 5

MOSSGIEL FARM

1784–1785

JOHN RICHMOND

At the age of seventeen, after attending school in Newmilns, John Richmond joined the law firm of John and Gavin Hamilton in Mauchline in 1782. He was employed as a clerk, working with Gavin Hamilton. Richmond and Burns were close friends and when the poet first arrived in Edinburgh, he lodged with Richmond, who had moved to Edinburgh to further his career as a lawyer.

Richmond later returned to Ayrshire and practised as a lawyer on his own account. He continued to correspond with the poet thereafter. Somewhat belatedly, he married Jenny Surgeoner in 1791, six years after she had borne him a daughter. The poet had earlier encouraged him to do the right thing by Jenny, advising him that his conduct was "highly inconsistent with the manly integrity I know your bosom glows with".

John Richmond died in 1831.

My name is John Richmond. I am forty-one years of age. I make this statement on 31st March 1806.

After I started my training as a lawyer with Gavin Hamilton, I became a close friend of Robert Burns, although he was six years older than me. I introduced Robert to my friend James Smith, the son of a local businessman, with whom we shared some uproarious times in Mauchline.

My former employer Mr Hamilton advised Robert's father throughout the dispute with his landlord, so I became familiar with all aspects of the litigation in respect of Lochlie, and the trauma endured by Robert's father on that account.

I would firstly like to clear up some confusion about what arrangements Mr Hamilton made with Robert and his brother Gilbert about the sublease of Mossgiel.

At the time, Mr Hamilton was the Earl of Loudon's factor. Mossgiel was but one of many properties on the Earl's estate, and Mr Hamilton had leased it from the Earl and built a new farmhouse on it, intending to use it as a sort of holiday retreat, but his wife Helen disliked the place. She was of the opinion that Mossgiel was in a miserable, cold location, a view which, with the benefit of hindsight, showed considerable perception. Robert and Gilbert's farming enterprise was beset with problems caused by the climate there.

Robert and Gilbert had started to badger Mr Hamilton in the autumn of 1783 about sub-leasing Mossgiel. They realised that their father was dying and they did not want to try to continue at Lochlie; the lease there was due to expire at Whitsunday 1784 in any event. I was present with Mr Hamilton when the discussions took place, and these had to take place in secret, as Robert and Gilbert did not want their father to be upset.

They also expressed an interest in some of Mr Hamilton's stock, and in October Robert wrote to him in the following terms:[1]

> Sir,
>
> As you are pleased to give us the offer of a private bargain of your cows you intend for sale, my brother and I this day took a look of them, and a friend with us, on whose judgment we could something depend, to enable us to form an estimate. If you are still intending to let us have them in that way, please appoint a day that we may wait on you, and either agree amongst ourselves or else fix on men to whom we may refer it, tho' I hope we will not need any reference.
>
> I am, Sir, your humble servant
>
> Machline, Oct. 18th 1793   Robert Burness
>
> PS Whatever of your dairy utensils you intend to dispose of, we will probably purchase.
>
> R.B.

As is now known, Robert and Gilbert subsequently took over Mossgiel with all the stock and implements. They were able to agree terms with Mr Hamilton without any reference to a third party. There was to be a sub-lease of the 118 acres at Mossgiel from Martinmas 1783 at an annual rent of £90.

Over the winter, not much work was needed at Mossgiel, and Robert and Gilbert did what was necessary while still staying at Lochlie. After their father died in February 1784 and his affairs were wound up, the Burns family moved to Mossgiel.

Although the outcome of the arbitration over Lochlie had been favourable to Robert's father, that dealt only with historic issues. There remained outstanding liabilities owed by William Burnes in respect of more recent rent and dilapidations, but Mr Hamilton argued successfully with David McClure's trustee in bankruptcy and the administrators of the Douglas Heron Bank that Burnes's farming assets could pass intact to the family as preferred creditors for past wages due.

Gilbert later described Mossgiel as an asylum for the Burns family but in the event, Mossgiel turned out to be less of a bargain than Robert and Gilbert originally thought.

In many ways it was surprising that Robert and Gilbert embarked on another farming enterprise. Earlier in the year Robert had written a letter[2] to his cousin James in Montrose. As can be seen, he was pessimistic about farming in Ayrshire and somewhat prophetic.

Dear Sir

> ... Farming is also at a very low ebb with us. Our lands, generally speaking, are mountainous and barren; and our Landholders, full of ideas of farming gathered from the English, and the Lothians, and other rich soils in Scotland, make no allowance for the odds of the quality of land, and consequently stretch us much beyond what, in the event, we will be found able to pay. We are also much at a loss for want of proper methods in our improvements of farming. Necessity compels us to leave our old schemes; and few of us have opportunities of being well informed in new ones ...
>
> Dear Sir, you affectionate Cousin,

Lochlee, 21st June 1793   Robt. Burns

When I saw them at the market in July, they both complained to me about their bad luck with the weather conditions at the farm. I understand that their first few months at Mossgiel were very difficult. Robert complained at the time of continually feeling unwell, although in view of what happened next in his personal life, he could not have been so unwell!

In November, there was a rumour going around that one of the Burns family's former servants was expecting a child by Robert. One evening, in the Whitefoord Arms, Gilbert confided in me. He told me that Robert's philandering had indeed caught up with him. Betsey Paton, a maidservant who had been with the Burns family at Lochlie, was claiming that Robert was the father of the child she was carrying. Robert had admitted he was responsible in that he had been intimate with her over the summer, and had said he was prepared to marry her.

Gilbert said that the girl had not moved with the family from Lochlie to Mossgiel, but had gone back to live with her parents at Largieside, although Robert had been seeing her regularly since. There had been a dreadful scene at Mossgiel when Robert confessed to the family that he was responsible. His mother liked the girl and was keen that she and Robert should marry, but Gilbert and his sisters thought she was rather a common person and Robert could do much better for himself. Robert's mother had been very upset, but Robert had reassured her that Betsey accepted that he had never promised to marry her. Robert had mollified his mother by reassuring her that he would make a financial provision for the child.

Our social life after work was best described as chaotic. Aside from drinking, dancing, gossiping and debating issues of the day, we formed a pretend law court which tried and passed judgment on local men thought to have misbehaved, principally with the fairer sex. Robert was the judge, I was the clerk of court, my friend James Smith, now working as the local draper, was the prosecutor and William

Hunter, the shoemaker, was the messenger at arms. We had fun putting our cases together, although our judgment was frequently clouded by alcohol. Robert captured the spirit of the society in this part of his poem 'The Court of Equity':[3]

> First, poet Burns he takes the chair,
> Allow'd by all his title's fair,
> And pass'd *nem. con.* without dissention,
> He has a duplicate pretension.
>
> Next merchant Smith, our worthy fiscal,
> To cow each pertinacious rascal,
> In this as every other state,
> His merit is conspicuous great.
>
> Richmond, the third, our worthy clerk,
> Our minutes regular to mark,
> A fit dispenser of the law,
> In absence of the ither twa.
>
> And fourth, our messenger at arms,
> When failing a' the milder terms;-
> Hunter, a willing hearty brither,
> Weel skill'd in dead and living leather.
>
> Without preamble, less or mair said,
> We body politic aforesaid,
> Wi' legal due whereas, and wherefore,
> Are thus appointed here to care for,
>
> At the instance of our constituents,
> To punish contraversing truants;
> Keeping a proper regulation,
> Within the lists of Fornication.

I myself could have been in the dock in the Court of Equity. I had been in a dalliance with a local girl, Jenny Surgeoner, and in December 1784 she told me she was pregnant and that I was the father. I was only nineteen at the time, and I had no thoughts of marriage. In January 1785 I had to endure being harangued in Mauchline Kirk on three Sundays by the Reverend William Auld for fornication. Robert looked on, no doubt amused, but at the same time mildly concerned that a similar fate awaited him.

Betsey Paton's daughter was born on 22nd May 1785 and named Elizabeth, though Robert called her Bess. Gilbert told me that although his relationship with Betsey had ended before the baby was born, Robert had arranged, presumably with Betsey's agreement, for the child to be brought up as part of the Burns household at Mossgiel. I think Robert's mother must have demanded that the child be cared for in this way.

I had spent quite a lot of time at the beginning of 1785 with Robert. The Kirk Session at Mauchline had a long-standing dispute with Mr Hamilton, the background to which is too convoluted to detail. In August 1784 the Session Clerk at Mauchline Kirk had leaked the terms of the Session Minutes to Mr Hamilton, and this had prompted him to write to the Session accusing them of having made assertions about his character which did not proceed from any good cause or foundation but from some private pique and ill nature. The Session regarded this letter as highly calumnious and injurious to their character, and demanded that Mr Hamilton prove what he claimed, or issue an apology.

Robert helped Mr Hamilton with the drafting of various letters to the Session and to the Presbytery of Glasgow, and the Presbytery issued a decision to the effect that the assertions about Mr Hamilton were to be excised from the Minutes.

William Auld, the Minister at Mauchline, and William Fisher, one of the elders, seemed determined to humiliate Mr Hamilton, and procured that the Session ignore the Presbytery direction and institute a number of further charges against him. Robert continued to assist Mr Hamilton in rebutting these charges, although the main credit for the successful outcome rests with Robert Aiken, the Ayr lawyer, who presented Mr Hamilton's case. Aiken was also a good friend of Robert's.

A resolution of sorts was achieved in July when the Session granted Mr Hamilton a certificate that he was "at present free from public scandal or ground of Church censure". You will observe, however, the careful wording; the Session was keeping its powder dry for a further shot at Mr Hamilton.

William Fisher had been one of the prime movers in the campaign against Mr Hamilton; indeed it was rumoured that it was as a result of his covert spying on Mr Hamilton that charges of travelling and working on the Sabbath and neglecting to read his Bible had been brought. This inspired Robert to compose his now famous 'Holy Willie's Prayer'[4] which includes the following verses about Mr Hamilton and Mr Aiken:

> Lord mind Gaun Hamilton's deserts;
> He drinks, and swears, and plays at cartes,
> Yet has sae mony takin arts
> Wi' Great and Sma',
> Frae God's ain Priest the people's hearts
> He steals awa.
>
> And when we chasten'd him therefore
> Thou kens how he bred sic a splore,
> And set the warld in a roar
> O' laughin at us:
> Curse Thou his basket and his store
> Kail and potatoes.

Lord hear my earnest cry and pray'r
Against that Presbytry of Ayr!
Thy strong right hand, Lord make it bare
Upo' their heads!
Lord visit them and dinna spare,
For their misdeeds!

O Lord, my God, that glib-tongu'd Aiken,
My very heart and flesh are quakin,
To think how I sat, sweatin, shakin,
And pish'd wi' dread,
While he, wi' hingin lip gaed sneakin
Held up his head.

Lord in Thy day o' vengeance try him!
Lord visit them wha did employ him!
And pass not in Thy mercy by them,
Nor hear their prayer,
But for Thy people's sake destroy them,
And dinna spare!

But, Lord, remember me and mine
Wi' mercies temporal and divine,
That I for grace and gear may shine,
Excell'd by nane!
And a' the glory shall be Thine –
Amen, Amen!

Robert had been somewhat depressed in the early part of the
year. It was noticeable that he recited little of his verse then, but he
seemed to buck up in the late summer and wrote some of his best
poetry over the following months.

In April Robert and I were diverted by another ecclesiastical
dispute. The ministers of two local parishes had fallen out over the

precise line of the boundary between their charges, and took the matter to the Presbytery of Irvine for a ruling. We attended the hearing and in open forum, the disputants, the Reverend Jock Russell of Kilmarnock and the Reverend Alexander Moodie of Riccarton, both lost their tempers and the debate degenerated into an exchange of abuse. Both are 'Auld Licht' ministers, of conservative views, so Robert, being of a 'New Licht', or liberal, persuasion, could not resist taunting them in these verses from his poem 'The Twa Herds':[5]

> O, Moodie, man, an' wordy Russell,
> How could you raise so vile a bustle;
> Ye'll see how New-Light herds will whistle,
> An' think it fine!
> The Lord's cause ne'er gat sic a twistle,
> Sin' I hae min'.

> Sic twa– O! Do I live to see't?
> Sic famous twa should disagree't,
> And names, like "villain", "hypocrite",
> Ilk ither gi'en,
> While New-Light herds, wi' laughin spite,
> Say neither's liein!

Moodie was a favourite target for Robert. In August the annual fair in Mauchline attracts a huge crowd, and in 1785 Moodie was the first speaker. Robert lampoons him in 'The Holy Fair':[6]

> Now a' the congregation o'er
> Is silent expectation;
> For Moodie speels the holy door,
> Wi' tidings o' damnation:
> Should Hornie, as in ancient days,
> 'Mang sons o' God present him,

The vera sight o' Moodie's face,
To 's ain het hame had sent him
Wi' fright that day.

Hear how he clears the points o' Faith
Wi' rattlin an' thumpin!
Now meekly calm, now wild in wrath,
He's stampin, an' he's jumpin!
His lengthen'd chin, his turn'd-up snout,
His eldritch squeel an' gestures,
O how they fire the heart devout,
Like cantharidian plaisters
On sic a day!

Moodie would feature again in Robert's life when Charles Maxwell-Campbell accused our friend Captain James Montgomery of seducing his wife and he became embroiled in the litigation.

Robert was really a very intellectual person. His library was extensive and included Adam Smith's *Theory of Moral Sentiments*, the book which Robert said was the basis for Smith's later work, *Wealth of Nations*. He often quoted from the former book, and wrote about it later in his life to his friend Captain Riddell:[7]

I intirely agree with that judicious philosopher, Mr Smith, in his excellent Theory of Moral Sentiments, that Remorse is the most painful sentiment that can embitter the human bosom. Any ordinary pitch of fortitude may bear up tolerably well under those calamities, in the procurement of which, we ourselves have had no hand; but when our own follies or crimes, have made us miserable & wretched, to bear up with manly firmness, and at the same time have a proper penitent sense of our misconduct, is a glorious effort of Self-command.

But, of course, there was a less serious side to his character. One evening in November, Robert, James Smith and I dropped in to a disreputable watering hole in Mauchline known as Poosie Nansie's, and there we took in a rumbustuous scene, following which Robert composed a poem, which was later entitled 'The Jolly Beggars'. When I next saw Robert I asked him to recite it, which he did effortlessly. I can honestly say that Robert's descriptions captured the scene to perfection. He left the manuscript of that poem with me together with some other scribblings when he went to Edinburgh.

There was a local tradition of having a dinner at the end of the harvest, when haggis was standard fare, at the home of the Kilmarnock lawyer David Shaw in Craigie Kirkdyke. At the dinner in 1785 a number of other lawyers were present, including Matthew Dickie and Alexander Walker from Edinburgh, William Paterson and William Brown from Kilmarnock, James Neil from Ayr, and myself. Robert was asked to say grace and after doing so, he recited his 'Address to the Haggis' which he said he had composed that week for the occasion.

On 28th October 1785, John, the younger brother of Robert and Gilbert, died at the age of sixteen years after a short illness. When I attended the funeral on 1st November, I told Robert that I was moving to Edinburgh to join William Wilson, Writer to the Signet, as his clerk. I just wanted to get away from Ayrshire, and see a bit more of the world. I also wanted to relieve the pressure on me to do the right thing by Jenny and her child. Robert confided in me that he was intending to put the Bachelors' Club and the 'Court of Equity' behind him anyway, as he was courting a local girl and they had become engaged. Of course, I later learned that this was Jean Armour whom Robert had met at a local dance about six months previously.

Later

During my first year in Edinburgh, my correspondence with Robert was sporadic. In February Robert had chastised me in a letter for failing to write to him, saying he could scarcely forgive my neglect, but that he was very busy with his poetry, having composed among others 'The Cotter's Saturday Night' and 'The Twa Dugs'. In July, while sympathising with me after I had suffered a period of illness, Robert pressed me to help raise subscribers for the Kilmarnock Edition, and announced his intention to emigrate to Jamaica. At the beginning of September, Robert sent me a copy of the Kilmarnock Edition, and implored me to keep it. He said his emigration had been postponed, but he hoped to sail at the end of that month. But within a few weeks, Robert told me he had changed his plans.

With the benefit of hindsight, I think this was influenced by the excellent sum that Robert earned from the Kilmarnock Edition, and the extent to which relations with the Armour family had improved. Robert confirmed to me that he had hoped to try for a second edition of his poetry with Wilson in Kilmarnock, but they were unable to agree terms, so he was determined to try in Edinburgh. Robert asked if he could share my lodgings in Edinburgh until he got settled. I, of course, was delighted to agree, and Robert arrived, exhausted, at my small room at Baxter's Close on 28th November 1786.

I stayed in Edinburgh for just under two years. After my employer Mr Wilson died in June 1787, I returned to practise in Mauchline.

I married Jenny Surgeoner in 1791, which legitimated our daughter Janet.

After Robert died, I remembered that he had left some papers with me. My nephew Thomas Stewart was a partner in a publishing house in Glasgow and I passed these to him, including a version of 'The Jolly Beggars'. That was perhaps a mistake on my part, as

Thomas was later sued by Robert's trustees. Thomas and his partner Meikle published several chapbooks of Robert's work over the following three years, the most outstanding including *The Jolly Beggars*, described as "printed from the author's own manuscript" and "one of the happiest efforts of his genius". They then produced a collation of the chapbooks entitled *The Poetical Miscellany*. Had Thomas rested on his laurels at that point, all would have been well, but in 1802 he came into possession of Robert's letters to his Edinburgh love known as Clarinda, which he and his then partner Macgoun published with catastrophic consequences. The ensuing litigation ruined him.

CHAPTER 6

MIGRATION

1786

GAVIN HAMILTON

The Kilmarnock Edition was dedicated to the lawyer Gavin Hamilton. His father had been a lawyer – clerk to the regality of Mauchline – but Gavin set up in practice on his own account in Mauchline.

He was a Freemason; his lodge was Lodge Loudon Kilwinning Newmilns.

Gavin Hamilton continued to correspond with the poet after his moves to Edinburgh and Dumfriesshire.

He died in 1805.

My name is Gavin Hamilton. I am a lawyer. I am fifty-three years of age. I make this statement on 31st March 1804. I had considerable involvement with the Burns family over the tenancy at Lochlie and the repercussions of the death of Robert's father. As is well known, I sub-leased Mossgiel to Robert and his brother Gilbert at the beginning of 1784 so they could make a fresh start after the traumas they had suffered at Lochlie. Farming at Mossgiel was a struggle for Robert and Gilbert but they paid my rent – £90 per annum – more or less on time.

I knew Robert socially as we were brother Freemasons. My Mother Lodge is Loudon Kilwinning Newmilns; in 1786 Robert was Depute Master of Lodge St James Tarbolton. I was well aware of his talent as a poet, and I also knew of his weakness for the fairer sex. It was no secret that he had fathered an illegitimate daughter by a servant girl called Betsey Paton, and that the child was being cared for at Mossgiel by Robert's widowed mother.

Gilbert Burns confided in me in the early part of the year about Robert's personal problems. He said that Robert had been walking out with Jean Armour, the daughter of local builder James Armour, and it was now apparent that she was pregnant. Robert and Jean had confessed to Jean's parents about the situation, and Jean's father had fainted. He had expressly forbidden Jean to marry Robert, and said while it was a shameful affair, he would arrange for Jean to be looked after, possibly by some relatives in Paisley. The Armours hoped the pregnancy could be kept secret.

According to Gilbert, Robert was uncertain about the effect of a letter he had written to Jean some time previously, which might have bound him to marry her. I agreed to see Robert to discuss it.

Robert seemed quite calm about the letter when I met him on 27th March, just before I introduced him to my Lodge as a joining member. He conceded that his situation was a little delicate – he already had one illegitimate child to support who he described as 'dear born Bess' and now he thought that Armour might be able to force him into a marriage which he certainly did not want. Robert had not kept a copy of the letter but he was able to give me the gist of what he had written.

I explained to him that a marriage can be constituted at law in one of three ways: firstly, by a declaration of present consent, in effect that the parties regarded themselves as married with immediate effect; secondly, by a promise to marry in the future followed by intercourse; and, thirdly, by cohabitation with habit and repute, which means living together with all the appearances of being husband and wife. From what Robert said, it looked as if the second could be his undoing if what he had written in the letter could be interpreted as a promise to marry. There had clearly been intercourse.

The leading case on these irregular marriages involved the Countess of Strathmore and her livery servant called George Forbes. Forbes claimed that he and the Countess were married, as they had lived as man and wife and a child had been born to them. A majority of the judges were of the view that an agreement to marry, even if the evidence of that came from a footman, if followed by intercourse, would make a valid marriage in Scotland.

I was about to expand on my views when Robert, as was his wont, suddenly lost interest in the issue, and went off at a tangent. I had been pressing him for some time to consider publishing a volume of his poetry. He produced from under his coat a copy of Milton's *Paradise Lost*, which had been published the previous year by John Wilson in Kilmarnock.

Robert said that, based on the quality of the copy of Milton's work, it looked as if Wilson could do justice to the task of publishing his poetry. I knew both John Wilson and his brother Peter. They were both Freemasons. I enthusiastically encouraged him to try to come to an arrangement with Wilson, which he agreed to do.

As is well known, for years I was in dispute with William Auld, the minister at Mauchline Kirk and the Kirk Session there. I did, however, have a friend on the Kirk Session who kept me up to date with developments, and at the beginning of April he told me that the Session had noted that Jean Armour was said to be with child, but she had left the area to reside elsewhere. The Session had determined that an enquiry should be instituted, but the interim report relayed the fact that her mother had assured the investigators she did not believe her daughter was with child. Mrs Armour said Jean was simply visiting friends in Paisley. At that stage, it seemed that there were to be no repercussions for Robert.

Proposals for publishing were agreed between Robert and Wilson, and on 15th April I received a letter from Robert enclosing an invitation to be a subscriber in respect of the first edition of his poems. The subscription blank[1] printed by Wilson had the benefit of brevity:

APRIL 14th, 1786

P R O P O S A L S

FOR PUBLISHING BY SUBSCRIPTION

S C O T C H P O E M S

B Y R O B E R T B U R N S

The Work to be elegantly Printed, in One Volume, Octavo.
Price Stitched Three shillings.

As the Author has not the most distant Mercenary view in Publishing, as foon as fo many Subfcribers appear as will defray the necessary Expence, the Work will be fent to the Prefs.

The same day that I received the invitation, my new clerk, who had replaced John Richmond, brought to me a letter from Robert dated 15th April 1786, written from Mossgiel. The relevant part was about the alleged actions of my good friend Robert Aiken, the Ayr lawyer, and was in the following terms:[2]

> Honoured Sir, Dear Benefactor,
>
> ... Apropos, old Mr Armour prevailed with him to mutilate that unlucky paper yesterday. Would you believe it? Tho' I had not a hope, nor even a wish, to make her mine after her damnable conduct, yet when he told me the names were all cut out of the paper, my heart died within me, and he cut my very veins with the news. – Perdition seize her falsehood and perjurious perfidy! but God bless her and forgive poor, once-dear, misguided girl. – She is ill-advised.... .
>
> Mossgiel, Saturday Morn.   Robt. Burns

I rode out to see Robert at Mossgiel. It was a miserable spring day, with the wind from the west driving horizontal rain, and I was soaked by the time I reached Mossgiel. There was no activity in the fields. Gilbert was in the barn mending a plough, but he simply waved to me as I passed.

Mrs Burns answered the door and I offered my condolences about her son John but she just shook her head sadly, and told me Robert was upstairs. A baby was crying in a crib in the corner; I presume it was Bess.

Gilbert had told me that since John died, Robert had one of the upstairs rooms to himself, doubling as a bedroom and study. Gilbert had moved into the other upstairs bedroom with his brother William.

I clattered up the wooden staircase and went into Robert's room. He was fast asleep on his bed. His desk under the window was covered with draft letters and poems. He woke up when I moved a chair to sit down. He was obviously angry but there was a calculating aspect to his questions which I had never been conscious of before.

He was concerned that the Armour affair might upset the arrangements for the publication of his poems. He wanted to know if he was now free of any commitment to Jean. I asked him how he knew that his letter had been mutilated. Robert said that Armour had sent him a note asking him to meet at the Whitefoord Arms, and when he arrived, Armour was waiting for him outside. Armour had waved his letter at him, and said Robert would never get to marry his daughter. Armour said that he'd been assured by Aiken that the letter was now null and void, and that Jean wanted him to know that she was glad to be rid of Robert.

I told Robert I was sure that Armour had made up this tale about the letter being mutilated, and I doubted if Aiken would even have agreed to see Armour, in view of the fact that he was such a close associate of Robert's. It was in any event almost inconceivable that Aiken would have done what was alleged, irrespective of the parties involved, for two reasons. Firstly, it would have had no certain effect, in that it would always have been possible, for a person relying on such a document as evidence, to raise an action of proving the terms of the document, which was a civil procedure by which the validity of a destroyed or mutilated document might be established and its terms re-declared by the Court in a form which is the equivalent in all respects of the original. Secondly, if a lawyer did mutilate the document, he would be exposing himself to criminal prosecution, conviction would lead to transportation to the Colonies. I was convinced – and I think I convinced Robert – that Armour himself had destroyed the letter, and made up the story about Aiken out of mischief.

Robert was relieved. In the event, he still maintained that he had never any desire to marry Jean, and would happily let the matter rest and concentrate on his poetry. He said he had another poker in the fire, though I did not fully understand what he meant by that until he revealed his affair with Highland Mary.

I learned later from Aiken direct that he had never even met Armour, far less mutilated the letter. Aiken obtained 145 subscriptions for Robert's work, and was thus by far the most successful promoter of what came to be known as the Kilmarnock Edition. I myself assembled forty orders.

The Kilmarnock Edition established Robert's reputation as both a poet of unusual talent and a shrewd observer of politics. As regards the latter, I draw attention to 'The Author's Earnest Cry and Prayer', his appeal on behalf of the Scottish distillers, which contains perceptive references to the leading politicians William Pitt and Charles Fox, as well as references to various figures in the legal profession, including Sir Adam Fergusson of Kilkerran, Henry Dundas, Thomas Erskine and Sir Ilay Campbell. The notion that Robert became familiar with the political and legal elite only after moving to Edinburgh is entirely misconceived.

About two weeks later, in the Whitefoord Arms, I found out about the emotional entanglement which he had referred to obliquely when we had met at Mossgiel.

Robert was in his cups. He had obviously been drinking for a while with James Smith the draper and John Richmond, who was on a visit back to Mauchline. I had been working late, and when I arrived, the carousing had already started. As I sat down with a glass, Robert apologised for his behaviour when I had met him at Mossgiel.

Robert said he had a new love. He had never met anyone like her.

She understood him, and she adored his poems. And as for lovemaking, she was second to none, and he was a man of experience. I am afraid Robert was prone to talk this way when he had overindulged.

This girl, who he called his 'Highland Mary', was a dairymaid at Coilsfield. Although he had met her only a month before, they were already planning to emigrate to Jamaica. Apparently Robert had had his fill of Ayrshire, farming, Armour, Kirk Sessions and propriety.

I could only sit, dumbfounded. Robert left us for a while and Richmond explained that Robert was concerned to secure a financial provision for Bess and also to prevent Armour from claiming his assets for Jean, and that he had advised Robert that it would be possible to transfer his assets to a guardian for Bess. What did I think?

I said I should probably have given him a better training in what advice to hand out to friends, but I would mull it over. I left the company in the Arms that night, as I was still stunned by Robert's news. I admit I did not give much thought to Richmond's idea about protecting Bess Paton's interests until the middle of June. My clerk brought me up to date with the Armour situation one Monday morning.

Apparently Jean had returned from Paisley and had been summoned by the Kirk Session to appear at a service, but she had failed to do so. The minister had read a letter from her, which had been recorded in the Minute Book, to the effect that Jean was heartily sorry that she had given and continued to give the Session trouble on her account. She now acknowledged that she was with child, and that Burns was the father.

The Session had decided that Robert would have to perform three penitential appearances. My clerk thought he would then be rebuked and called upon to say that having sinned by fornication he would do so no more. I must say I smiled inwardly at this, knowing what I did about Highland Mary.

This did prompt me, however, to give some thought to the Bess Paton problem. I was uneasy about this as Armour and I were both in Mauchline, so I recommended that Robert consult William Chalmers, an Ayr lawyer.

Chalmers duly prepared a transfer[3] which was signed by Robert on 22nd July. It was in the following terms:

> Know all men by these presents that I Robert Burns in Mossgiel:
>
> Whereas I intend to leave Scotland and go abroad, and having acknowledged myself the father of a child named Elizabeth, begot upon Elizabeth Paton in Largieside:
>
> And whereas Gilbert Burns in Mossgiel, my brother, has become bound, and hereby binds and oblidges himself to aliment, clothe and educate my said natural child in a suitable manner as if she was his own, in case her Mother chuse to part with her, and that until she arrive at the age of fifteen years:
>
> THEREFORE and to enable the said Gilb. Burns to make good his said engagement, wit. ye me to have, assigned, disponed, conveyed and made over to, and in favors of, the said Gilbert Burns, his Heirs, Executors and Assignees, who are always to be bound in like manner with himself, all and Sundry Goods, Gear, Corns, Cattle, Horses, Nolt, Sheep, Household furniture, and all other moveable effects of whatever kind that I shall leave behind me on my departure from the kingdom, after allowing for my part in the conjunct debts due by the said Gilbert Burns and me as joint Tacksmen of the farm of Mossgiel.
>
> And particularly, without prejudice to the foregoing generality, the profits that may arise from the publication of my Poems presently in the Press.

And also, I hereby dispone and convey to him in trust for behoof of my said natural daughter, the Copyright of said Poems in so far as I can dispose of the same by law, after she arrives at the above age of fifteen years complete.

Surrogating and substituting the said Gilbert Burns, my brother and his aforesaids in my full right, title, room and place of the whole premises, with power to him to intromit with, and dispose upon the same at pleasure, and in general to do every other thing in the Premises that I could have done myself, before granting hereof, but always with and under the conditions before expressed.

And I oblidge myself to warrand this disposition and assignation from my own proper fact and deed allenarly.

Consenting to the Registration hereof in the Books of Council and Session, or any other Judge's Books competent, therein to remain for preservation.

Robert Burns

The deed which Robert had signed was timely, because Armour obviously heard about Robert's plans to emigrate and determined to take steps to protect the interests of his daughter by arranging for the issue of a writ *in meditatione fugae*.

Gilbert brought the document to me, a copy having been left at Mossgiel. By the time the sheriff officers arrived at Mossgiel, Robert had fled as, by chance, one of his friends had found out what Armour was thinking of doing, and forewarned Robert.

I explained to Gilbert that if someone has a financial claim against another person, a *fugae* warrant gives power to imprison that person if he is intending to evade his liability by fleeing the country. The imprisoned person remains incarcerated until either he finds caution, which means that he or someone else lodges funds in court to cover the potential liability, or the claim is decided on by the court. The writ issued[4] was in Jean's name and in the following terms:

UNTO THE SHERIFF OF THE COUNTY OF AYR

PETITION

of

JEAN ARMOUR, a resident of Mauchline,

PETITIONER

for

Warrant to apprehend ROBERT BURNS, farmer in Mossgiel, Mauchline

HUMBLY SHEWETH:-

(One)   That the Petitioner, Jean Armour, is pregnant to the said Robert Burns in consequence of sexual connection which took place between them.

(Two)   That the Petitioner has been credibly informed, and in her conscience believes, that the said Robert Burns is presently in meditatione fugae and about to leave Scotland to take up employment in Jamaica, in order to avoid the Petitioner's lawful claim against him for inlying expenses, and aliment to the child; and

(Three)   That the Petitioner will thereby be defrauded or disappointed of her claim against the said Robert Burns for such inlying expenses and aliment.

MAY IT THEREFORE please your Lordship to take the Petitioner's oath to the verity of the statements made in this Petition; and thereon to grant warrant to apprehend and bring the said Robert Burns before your Lordship for examination; and thereafter to commit him to the prison of Ayr, therein to be detained until he finds sufficient caution, acted in your Lordship's Court Books, de judicio sisti in any action for payment of the said inlying expenses and aliment, and consequents, which may be raised against him, at the instance of the Petitioner; and in case the said Robert Burns has left or may leave your Lordship's jurisdiction, to recommend to all other Judges and Magistrates to concur in your Lordship's said warrant. And in the event of opposition to find the said Robert Burns liable in expenses, and to decern therefor.

According to Justice, &c.

I advised Gilbert that all Robert could do was try to negotiate with Armour, and I warned him that the action came so soon after the Assignation that Armour might, in fact, try to reduce it, meaning to make it void, as being intended to defeat Jean's claim.

Gilbert asked if Robert needed to respond to the Petition, and I said I could not assist as I was an officer of the court and I could not take instructions from someone hiding from the authorities. I said I would sound out Armour about what he wanted for Jean, on the basis that I had a channel of communication with Robert, though I did not know where he was.

And that is how it was left. I invited Armour to meet with me but he never responded.

The Kilmarnock Edition was printed and ready for distribution on 30th July. Mr Wilson printed 612 copies priced at three shillings each. The subscription monies for the 428 advance sales were collected in August and, by the end of the month, Wilson had sold all but thirteen of the remainder. Robert kindly dedicated the edition to me.

By the middle of August, Robert had come out of hiding and I met him in at the Whitefoord Arms. He told me that he was no longer very apprehensive about the action against him initiated by Jean on the instructions of her father, and he was now back staying with the family at Mossgiel. He had in fact met Jean and was sure she would now marry him if he asked her to do so, but he was fixed in his idea of emigration to Jamaica to start a new life unburdened by previous involvements with Betsey and Jean.

Jean Armour gave birth to twins in Mauchline on Sunday 3rd September. My clerk brought me a copy of the Session Clerk's record:[5]

> Burns, Robert, Tenant in Mossgiel, and Jean Armour had Twin Children Born 3rd and Baptized 5th Septr called Robert and Jean.

Robert then prevaricated about emigrating. It was now months after the date of his intended departure from Greenock and he was still at Mossgiel. I met him in Kilmarnock about a week after his twins were born. He told me that the children were well, and that Armour even allowed him to call at his house to see them. Armour had abandoned his action against Robert.

I asked if he was going to support Jean, or was he still involved with Highland Mary. He became somewhat evasive at that point. He said the girl and he were still in touch, and the plan was to meet up in Greenock before leaving for Jamaica. But he was thinking of waiting on at Mossgiel until the harvest was in. Gilbert could do with the help, and anyway he was exploring the idea of a second edition of his poems.

On 26th October Robert was made an honorary member of Lodge St John Kilmarnock. I suspect the success of the *Kilmarnock Edition* was a contributory factor.

I met Gilbert and Robert at the beginning of November. They were full of complaints. Gilbert moaned about another unsuccessful harvest, and Robert was apoplectic about John Wilson, who had declined to finance a second edition of his work. Wilson had said he would meet the cost of the printing, which would have been about £16, but he wanted Robert to supply the paper, and Robert did not have the £27 needed for that. Robert was determined to find another publisher in Edinburgh, where he might secure more wealthy subscribers.

I suggested that he could not have spent all the profit of the Kilmarnock Edition, but he said he had settled some liabilities, including making a provision for Bess Paton. He was going to send Betsey Paton to see me, to execute a Discharge of any liability to her.

Robert turned away to speak to some subscribers who had come into the Inn. I took the opportunity to ask Gilbert if there was any other reason why Robert was reconsidering his plans. Had there been a falling out with Highland Mary?

Gilbert said that Robert still had his ticket for Jamaica, but he would be going on his own if he decided to emigrate. He had been told that Highland Mary had died of the typhus while waiting for him in Greenock. Gilbert thought it was just as well as, not for the first time, his sisters and he were of the opinion that Robert's conquest was entirely unsuitable. Some of Robert's friends had tried to tell him that the girl known as Highland Mary was a woman of loose morals, and was conducting an affair with his brother Freemason Captain James Montgomery at the same time as she was having relations with him. Robert did not believe them, so they had taken him to the inn where Montgomery and she were having an assignation, and he saw them emerge from the same bedroom. But Robert had been blind to this, and had persevered with her. Gilbert thought that the Jamaica idea had become so intertwined with Highland Mary that Robert would now abandon it, and he was proved to be correct in this.

I believe it is possible Robert may be referring to Highland Mary as 'My Montgomerie's Peggy' in the following passage[6] which he later wrote to his friend Captain Robert Riddell. I understand that Mary's christened name was Margaret, and Peggy is the name often given to a Margaret. It may, of course, be yet another of Robert's conquests!

> My Montgomerie's Peggy was my deity for six, or eight months. She had been bred, tho', as the world says, without any just pretence for it, in a style of life rather elegant. But, as Vanbrugh says in one of his comedies, my "Dam'd Star found me out" there too, for though I began the affair merely in a gaitié de cœur, or, to tell the truth, what would scarcely be believed, a vanity of showing my parts in Courtship, particularly my abilities at a Billet-doux, which I always piqu'd myself upon, made me lay siege to her; and when, as I always do in my foolish gallantries, I had battered myself into a very warm affection for her, she told me, one day in a flag of truce, that her fortress had been for some time before the rightful property of another; but, with the greatest friendship and politeness, she offered me every alliance, except actual possession. I found out

afterwards, that what she told me of a pre-engagement was really true; but it cost me some heart Achs to get rid of the affair.

Robert always fancied himself as an amateur lawyer and at the end of November, William Chalmers, the Ayr lawyer who had prepared the Assignation to Gilbert, showed me a writ Robert had drafted to accompany one of his bawdy ballads. His aptitude for mocking lawyers comes through the wording of the writ:[7]

IN THE NAME OF THE NINE, AMEN.

We, Robert Burns, by virtue of a Warrant from Nature, bearing date the Twenty fifth day of January, Anno Domini one thousand seven hundred and fifty nine, Poet Laureat, and Bard-in-Chief, in and over the Districts and Countries of Kyle, Cunningham, and Carrick, of old extent,–

To our trusty and well-beloved William Chalmers and John McAdam, Students and Practitioners in the ancient and mysterious Science of Confounding Right and Wrong.

RIGHT TRUSTY–Be it known unto you, that whereas in the course of our care and watchings over the Order and Police of all and sundry the Manufacturers, Retainers, and Vendors of Poesy; Bards, Poets, Poetasters, Rhymers, Jinglers. Songsters, Ballad-singers, etc., etc., etc., etc., male and female–

We have discovered a certain nefarious, abominable, and wicked Song or Ballad, a copy whereof We have here inclosed; Our Will therefore is, that Ye pitch upon and appoint the most execrable individual of that most execrable Species known by the appellation, phrase, and nickname of "The Deil's Yell Nowte", and after having caused him to kindle a fire at the Cross of Ayr, ye shall, at noontide of the day, put into the said wretch's merciless hands the said copy of the said nefarious and wicked Song, to be consumed by fire in presence of all Beholders, in abhorrence of, and terrorem to, all such Compositions and Composers. And this in no wise leave ye undone, but have it executed in every point as this Our Mandate bears, before the twenty-fourth current, when in person We hope to applaud your faithfulness and zeal.

Given at Mauchline this twentieth day of November, Anno Domini one thousand seven hundred and eighty six.

GOD SAVE THE BARD!

Betsey Paton made an appointment to see me at the end of November. She refused to tell me how much Robert had given her for Bess – I was told later it was £20 – but said she was perfectly satisfied with the settlement and was happy to discharge Robert from further liability. I drafted a Discharge[8] which she signed on 1st December:

> I ELIZABETH PATON, residing in Largieside Whereas Affirms the twenty second day of May MDCC Eighty five years I brought furth a female child to Robert Burns in Mossgiel which he acknowledged satisfied the Church and got the child christened by the name of Elizabeth and since that period hath given me a pretty liberal allowance for inlying charges and maintenance and clothing to this date; And now, by agreement betwixt him and I, Burns hath made payment to me of a certain sum of money, which I have accepted and hereby accept in full and compleat

payment and satisfaction for all board, wages, clothing and education which I can claim for the said Elizabeth our child until she arrives at the age of Ten years compleat, the said Robert Burns being to free me of any expense attending thereafter, Therefore I not only exoner and discharge the said Robert Burns of all claims I have against him for maintenance clothing and education of the said child till it arrives at the foresaid age of ten years compleat, but also promise and engage to be carefully attending to the health and education of the said child till that period In Witness Whereof these presents wrote against a fourpence stamp by Gavin Hamilton, Writer, Mauchline are subscribed by me by initials, being my ordinary means of signature, at Mauchline on the First day of December seventeen hundred and eighty five before these witnesses James Smith, Merchant in Mauchline and the said Gavin Hamilton.

James Smith, Witness	Elizabeth
	E.P.
Gavin Hamilton, Witness	Paton

Gilbert then demanded of me to advise where he stood. He had been appointed as guardian of Bess Paton, and Robert had assigned all his moveable estate to him for the purpose of maintaining Bess until she attained fifteen years. He was unsure about the effect of the Discharge on that.

He said that the Assignation was predicated on Robert emigrating, which was not now going to happen. Robert had left for Edinburgh to organise the second edition of his poems, and was concerned about the copyright. Robert was adamant that the Discharge superseded the Assignation.

I said it was debatable, but I suggested that he grant a Retrocession of the rights assigned by Robert. I would narrate that Robert was not now intending to emigrate, that Betsey was happy with the settlement Robert had made in her favour, and that therefore Gilbert would transfer back to Robert the rights he transferred to him as guardian of Bess.

Gilbert confirmed it was important to Robert that he was able to deal with his copyright, so, for what it was worth, I prepared a Retrocession[9] in the following terms:

> I GILBERT BURNS, residing at Mossgiel, Mauchline Considering that by Assignation in my favour dated the 22nd day of July 1786 my brother ROBERT BURNS, residing at Mossgiel, aforesaid assigned, disponed, conveyed and made over to, and in favors of me All and Sundry Goods, Gear, Corns, Cattle, Horses, Nolt, Sheep, Household furniture, and all other moveable effects of whatever kind that he might leave behind him on his departure from the kingdom, after allowing for his part in the conjunct debts due by him and me as joint Tacksmen of the farm of Mossgiel. And particularly, without prejudice to the foregoing generality, the profits that might arise from the Publication of his Poems, and also the Copyright of said Poems. And Considering that the purpose of the said Assignation was to enable me to aliment, clothe and educate his natural child Elizabeth Paton in a suitable manner as if she was my own; And Considering that ELIZABETH PATON in Largieside, mother of his said natural child Elizabeth Paton by Discharge dated the first day of December One thousand seven hundred and eighty six has acknowledged receipt of a certain sum of money from my said brother and granted a

discharge of all liability in respect of the said natural child; And Considering that the said Assignation in my favour is consequently no longer required NOW THEREFORE I Hereby Retrocess to and in favour of the said ROBERT BURNS the whole premises of the said Assignation; Surrogating and substituting the said Robert Burns, my brother and his foresaids in my full right, title, room and place of the whole premises, with power to him to intromit with, and dispose upon the same at pleasure; And I oblidge myself to warrand this disposition and assignation from my own proper fact and deed allenarly. Consenting to the Registration hereof in the Books of Council and Session, or any other Judge's Books competent, therein to remain for preservation.

Gilbert signed the Retrocession, and I sent Robert a copy. By this time, he had moved to Edinburgh, and was lodging with John Richmond, who had left Mauchline under a bit of a cloud because of his entanglement with Jenny Surgeoner and her resultant pregnancy.

Later

After Robert moved to Edinburgh, we corresponded for a couple of years. In 1787 Robert kept me informed about progress in James Montgomery's long-running dispute with Maxwell-Campbell, in which the latter sought damages from Montgomery for seducing his wife. That was a case in which I became embroiled personally.

Later that year, Robert visited my relations at Harviestoun on one of his tours, and he upbraided me for failing to keep in touch with my family.

In 1788 our relationship came under strain. I consider it was because I was Gilbert's landlord at Mossgiel and he was struggling financially. Robert started including sarcastic comments in letters to me, and when I very reasonably asked him to stand as guarantor for Gilbert, he sent me a hurtful refusal. That was, in effect, the end of our friendship.

CHAPTER 7

HIGH SOCIETY

1787

HENRY MACKENZIE

Henry Mackenzie was born in 1745 in Edinburgh. His father, Joshua Mackenzie, was a distinguished doctor. Henry was educated at the Royal High School and the University of Edinburgh, and was then apprenticed to George Inglis of Redhall, the Crown Agent for Exchequer matters. He became Inglis' partner and succeeded him as Crown Agent.

He was regarded as a literary giant of the era, and in a painting by Thomas Faed RA at Abbotsford, the home of Sir Walter Scott, he is pictured together with, among others, his friends William Wordsworth, Sir Adam Ferguson, James Hogg, Sir William Allan RA, Thomas Campbell, Archibald Constable, J. G. Lockhart, Lord Jeffrey, Sir David Wilkie and Scott himself.

Henry Mackenzie died in 1831.

My name is Henry Mackenzie. I am a lawyer and a writer. I am sixty years of age. I make this statement on 31st March 1806.

Dugald Stewart, Professor of Moral Philosophy at the University of Edinburgh, is a good friend of mine. In August 1786, during the university vacation, he was at Catrine Bank, near Mauchline, his country house. His friend Doctor John MacKenzie, who had cared for Robert Burns's father in the period up to his demise, sent Dugald a copy of the Kilmarnock Edition of Robert Burns's poems. He was impressed and later invited Burns to dine with him at Catrine Bank.

When Dugald returned to Edinburgh for the start of the new university year he brought his copy of the Kilmarnock Edition and loaned it to me to review. At the time I was editing *The Lounger*, a literary periodical which was published by my brother Freemason, William Creech, the Edinburgh publisher. My review of Burns's poetry was published at the beginning of December, and as I read it now, with the benefit of hindsight, while it captures the genius of the poet, its tone is patronising.

Burns arrived in Edinburgh around the beginning of December 1786. I met him for the first time on 7th December when he attended a meeting of Freemasons at Lodge Canongate Kilwinning. I was introduced to him by Dugald, and at the meeting Burns met, among others, James Cunningham, the Earl of Glencairn, Harry Erskine (Dean of the Faculty of Advocates), William Brodie (now universally referred to as 'Deacon Brodie'), the music seller James Johnson, my fellow lawyers William Dunbar and the young Robert Ainslie, and Louis Cauvin, a teacher of the French language who later gave Burns lessons in French. Creech was also present.

The Earl of Glencairn had a previous connection with Burns in that it was he, as patron of Kilmarnock parish, who had chosen a conservative minister to fill a church vacancy there in 1785, and had thus inspired Burns to write his satirical poem 'The Ordination' which, although not included in the Kilmarnock Edition, was widely circulated in Ayrshire and had come to Glencairn's attention. This possible faux pas on the part of Burns had no ill effect, as Glencairn was one of his most enthusiastic supporters, and it was he who introduced Burns to Creech.

Publishing my periodical *The Lounger* was but a small part of Creech's business. At the time he had a wide circle of authors under his wing, and he had a profitable joint venture arrangement with the London publishers Cadell and Davies. Dugald was one of his closest friends, and I have no doubt he encouraged Creech to be generous with Burns on proposals for a second edition. However, matters developed and in short order, Creech and Burns reached an agreement in principle under which Creech printed the subscription bills, just as John Wilson had done for Burns's Kilmarnock Edition, but left Burns to make his own arrangements for the printing and binding with William Smellie and William Scott who were also Freemasons at Lodge Canongate Kilwinning. The following appeared on 14th December, only two weeks after Burns had arrived in Edinburgh:[1]

In the Press, and speedily will be Published

BY WILLIAM CREECH

Elegantly printed in one volume 8vo, price 5s. in boards,

A SECOND EDITION of
BURNS's POEMS

With corrections and large Additions
This book is printed by subscription for the sole bene
fit of the author – As several private subscription papers
are in circulation, it is requested that, when filled up,
they may be transmitted to Mr Creech

Burns's initial impression of Creech was that he was as a multi-faceted character, idle but shrewd, mean but basically good hearted. That opinion was not universally shared. Maria Riddell, one of Burns's inamoratas during his time in Dumfries, later described Creech as someone to be avoided like plague or pestilence and a great rogue as well as an intolerable pedant. Burns himself came to despise Creech owing to his evasiveness and delays in settling the royalties due from the Edinburgh Edition.

The nobility and the literati of Edinburgh were enthusiastic to meet Burns after his arrival in the capital. I know, for example, that he was a regular at parties hosted by the Duchess of Gordon, and spent New Year's Eve in 1786 at a dinner in the company of Lord Monboddo and his family. Burns was very taken by Lord Monboddo's daughter Eliza, who was a prominent beauty of the time. In a letter to William Chalmers, the Ayr lawyer, he described her as the "heavenly" Miss Burnett.

In what might be described as the high society of Edinburgh, people tend to make vague promises of support to artists and writers. Burns was rather naïve. When he was introduced to several members of the Caledonian Hunt, he misinterpreted their comments and was convinced that all members of the Hunt were to subscribe to the Edinburgh Edition and pay one guinea each. In fact, the Earl of Glencairn had simply advised Burns that he would put a proposal for subscription to the Hunt, and in January they did agree to subscribe to 100 copies at five shillings each, the normal subscription price.

In January William Smellie introduced Burns to the Crochallan Fencibles, a club which met once a week at Daniel Douglas's Tavern at the top of Anchor Close. It consisted of literary men of culture, including many advocates. The name was an amusement because there were so many military volunteer corps in Edinburgh at the time, and the members teased out the joke by awarding themselves pretended military rank. William Dunbar held the rank of Colonel, and the advocate Charles Hay, later Lord Newton, was a Major and Muster-Master General. Hay and Smellie were deputed to test Burns – to dispense the customary initiation treatment (rudeness) to test his humour.

Burns took the insults in good part and passed the test. He gave as good as he got. Smellie was a member of the Society of Antiquaries and the Royal Society of Edinburgh, but he was a rather dishevelled character, and Burns composed a retaliatory description of the printer:[2]

WILLIAM SMELLIE – A SKETCH

Crochallan came:
The old cock'd hat, the brown surtout the same;
His grisly beard just bristling in its might
('Twas four long nights and days from shaving-night!):
His uncomb'd, hoary locks, wild-staring, thatch'd
A head for thought profound and clear unmatch'd:
Yet, tho' his caustic wit was biting rude,
His heart was warm, benevolent and good.

Burns struggled to come to terms with the fact that in Edinburgh he was a small fish in a large pond. As an example, he described how he felt he had been insulted when he had sought an estimate from another company for printing his second edition. He felt he had given a good account of his proposal, but the proprietor clearly had no idea who he was, and had made it perfectly obvious that he regarded Burns as a time-waster.

In addition, he was very unsure of himself, always coming up with different ideas about how he should spend his life, and agonising about his future. We had a discussion after his admission to my Lodge when he firstly told me that he had raised with our brother Freemason Patrick Miller of Dalswinton the possibility of taking a lease of a property in Dumfries, and in the same conversation he asked for my opinion about his joining the Excise. The latter idea was a notion he had nurtured for some time. I know that he had raised it the previous year with his friend the agricultural improver Sir John Whitefoord, a brother Freemason at Lodge St James Tarbolton, who had said that while he would help Burns with the Excise idea in any way he could, his feeling was that if Burns were able to raise some capital from a second edition, he would be better advised to lay it out in stocking a small farm. That turned out to be poor advice. Incidentally, Whitefoord was another landowner whose family estates had to be sold as a result of his involvement with the Douglas Heron Bank.

Burns asked me whether he was free to dispose of the copyright in his works. Protection had been given to a writer's copyright by the Statute of Anne 1709, which gave copyright to an author and his assignees for a period of fourteen years from the date of first publication, and for a further fourteen years should the author be alive at the end of the first term. Burns told me there was a complication regarding his copyright ownership, and explained to me the history of his Assignation the previous year to his brother Gilbert and the subsequent Retrocession. I advised Burns that although I had doubts about the effect of the Retrocession, he should proceed on the assumption that the copyright in his poems was now his, in view of the fact that his obligation to Bess, for which he had given the original Assignation to Gilbert, had now been discharged.

At the beginning of March Burns introduced me to Captain James Montgomery, a brother Freemason at Lodge St James Tarbolton. Montgomery and Burns were friends, although I was told by John Richmond that both had been rivals for the affections of a local beauty in Mauchline.

Montgomery was involved in a notorious long-running legal case and Burns wanted to support him as his case concerned a very important point of law which was to be debated at the Court of Session. Lord Swinton, the same judge who had refused Burns's father's Bill of Suspension in 1783 on the conclusion of an arbitration relating to his lease, heard the argument in the first instance and then reported the case to the Inner House for a decision.

Montgomery had seduced Eleanora, the wife of Charles Maxwell-Campbell, and she had eloped with him in July 1783, bearing him a son in November 1784. Maxwell-Campbell was much older than his wife, and around the time she had left him, he had been embroiled in financial difficulties resulting in his imprisonment for debt in Dumfries. He then signed a trust deed in favour of his creditors. Having been discharged from these liabilities, he decided to sue Montgomery for damages. Maxwell-Campbell circulated bills in Edinburgh and Ayrshire in February 1786 to the effect that Captain James Montgomery, late of the 93rd Regiment of Foot, was a coward and a lying scoundrel, which he could prove. This was defamation of Montgomery's character, but he took no action, perhaps because it was true. It was Maxwell-Campbell who went to court, suing Montgomery for £5,000 damages and £100 expenses, although how he thought he could afford to do so is a mystery, as he himself was once again in debt.

One of his creditors, David Guthrie, a local farmer, had a decree against him for £120 14s. plus interest.

Burns sat with Montgomery in court and listened intently to the arguments. The advocate acting for Montgomery was Charles Hay of the Crochallan Fencibles. He argued that the action was not competent on the basis that no husband could claim damages against either his wife or her paramour if he could be seen to have acquiesced as a married man to the state of affairs by declining to divorce his adulterous wife. Hay insisted that it was necessary for a claimant in these circumstances to show that he actually felt the alleged injury which could be demonstrated only by his outward actions. If such a man failed to divorce his wife, a woman who, as he alleged, had "prostituted her person to a stranger, and thereby incurred the risk of introducing a spurious brood to inherit, or at least share, the fortune which ought to descend to her lawful issue",[3] then a suspicion must be entertained that there was a good reason for her actions. Hay speculated that such reasons could include:

> that there has been a private understanding between the wife and her husband, that she should yield favours to a gallant, on purpose that there may be an opportunity of fleecing him; or that there have been such improprieties in the husband's conduct, as deter him from calling his wife to account for her conduct, lest she should be able to recriminate, and to paint his conduct in such a light as to forfeit him of any claim of reparation, either against her or her supposed gallant, and thereby, though it may not be possible to justify, at least to palliate her own misconduct.[4]

Their Lordships grew restive at this line of argument, which rather outraged them. Alexander Wight, the advocate acting for

Maxwell-Campbell, pointed out that there were obvious situations in which it would not be in the interests of the cuckolded husband to institute divorce proceedings. He gave as an example:

> Pecuniary considerations, upon which the support of a family may depend, may also in particular cases render it unadvisable in a husband to push matters to extremity against his wife, although possessed of full proof of her guilt.[5]

The Court found in favour of Maxwell-Campbell's argument, with a further hearing scheduled to fix the damages and expenses. The following is an excerpt from Burns's letter in March 1787[6] reporting the outcome to his Mauchline lawyer friend, Gavin Hamilton:

Dear Sir

> … Poor Captain Montgomerie is cast. Yesterday it was tried whether the husband could proceed against the unfortunate lover without first divorcing his wife, and their Gravities on the Bench were unanimously of opinion that Maxwell may prosecute for damages directly, and need not divorce his wife at all if he pleases; and Maxwell is immediately, before the Lord Ordinary to prove, what I dare say will never be denied, the Crim-Con and then their Lordships will modify the damages, which I suppose will be pretty heavy, as their Wisdoms have expressed great abhorrence of my gallant Right Worshipful Brother's conduct.
>
> I am ever, Dr Sir, your oblidged

Edinburgh, 8th March 1787   Robert Burns

Burns was receiving advice on his future from a number of quarters at this time. He had of course been accustomed to a very modest annual income; he told me farming brought him about £10 per annum.

Mrs Frances Dunlop, widow of John Dunlop of Dunlop in Ayrshire and a patron of Burns, approached the famous economist Adam Smith on his behalf. Smith had been appointed a Commissioner of Customs. She then suggested to Burns that he become a Salt Officer. Their income was about £30 to £40, and Salt Officers were not despised in the same way as excise officers.

This was an avenue which Burns might have pursued, but sadly, when he called to see him with his introduction from Mrs Dunlop, Smith had gone to London. For some reason Burns did not take up the matter with him on his return, despite the fact that he was an admirer of Adam Smith's work.

Around this time I was acting as a kind of arbiter in advising on the publishing contract between Burns and Creech. The Edinburgh Edition was published by Creech on Tuesday, 17th April, and that day we had a meeting which was recorded as follows:[7]

17th April 1787

MEMORANDUM OF AGREEMENT BETWIXT MR CREECH AND MR BURNS, respecting the property of Mr Burns's Poems

By advice of friends, Mr. Burns, having resolved to dispose of the property of his Poems and having consulted with Mr Henry McKenzie upon the subject, Mr Creech met with Mr Burns at Mr McKenzie's house upon Tuesday, the 17th April 1787, in the evening, and they three having retired and conversed upon the subject, Mr Burns and Mr Creech referred the sum, to be named by Mr McKenzie as being well acquainted with matters of this kind, when Mr McKenzie said he thought Mr Burns should have a hundred guineas for the property of his Poems.

Mr Creech said that he agreed to the proposal, but as Scotland was now amply supplied with the very numerous editions now printed, he could write to Mr Caddell of London, to know if he would take a share of the Book, but at any rate Mr Burns should have the money named by Mr McKenzie, which Mr Burns most cordially agreed to, and to make over the property upon these terms, whenever Mr Creech required him.

Creech did not receive a timeous response from Caddell, so the following Monday a supplementary minute[8] was prepared:

Upon Monday, the 23rd of April 1787, Mr Creech informed Mr Burns that he had remained in Town expecting Mr Caddell's answer, for three days, as to his taking a share of the property of the Poems; but that he had received no answer; yet he would, as formerly proposed and agreed to, take the whole matter upon himself, that Mr Burns might be at no uncertainty in the matter. Upon this, both parties considered the transaction as finished.

I advised Burns that he was unlikely to get much in the way of payment from Creech for a few months, and while he was frustrated not to have any income, as he wanted to help his brother Gilbert with his farming enterprise, he accepted that he would need to press Creech himself. I think Burns felt guilty about in effect abandoning

Gilbert at Mossgiel. I do know that Gilbert did later receive a substantial loan from his brother.

A few months later Burns was back at the Court of Session supporting his friend Captain Montgomery and his mistress Eleanora Maxwell-Campbell. The "pecuniary considerations" which had been referred to in the earlier hearing of her husband's action now came to the fore in an action brought by Eleanora Maxwell-Campbell against her husband and his creditors, and the creditors of both her late father and her brother. She claimed that her husband had represented to her that he had an annual income of £500 when she was induced to marry him, whereas the reality was that he was insolvent, and he now refused to maintain her. Skerrington Estate, her own family's property, produced a substantial income, but both her father and brother were insolvent too, and the estate had been sequestrated (as it happens, with Gavin Hamilton, Burns's lawyer friend, appointed to factor it). An argument developed as to who was entitled to be paid out of the rents from a choice of potential beneficiaries, including Mrs Maxwell-Campbell, her children, her husband, his creditors, and the creditors of her own family. In the event she was successful in obtaining an award.

Maxwell-Campbell himself returned to the Court of Session in December. In attempting to prove his case against Montgomery, he had cited as witnesses to confirm his wife's adultery the local parish minister, Alexander Moodie, and also Gavin Hamilton (both of whom objected to being compelled as witnesses). Moodie, an 'Auld Licht' minister, was well known to Burns from his Mauchline days and is referred to in various of his poems. He was Mrs Maxwell-Campbell's minister, and had baptised her son Jamie, the alleged bastard child born after she separated from her husband, and he had met with her while visiting his parishioners. Moodie considered it would be improper to reveal what had passed in private conversations between them. Hamilton, already burdened with the conflict of interest through being the Skerrington Estate factor, claimed he was also acting as Montgomery's agent. The Court found that neither should be compelled to give evidence.

I have been criticised for acting as I did between Burns and Creech, the perception being that I had a conflict of interest, but I am satisfied that the bargain struck was a reasonable one at the time for both parties. That is what one should hope for from an arbiter. Burns's friend Mrs Dunlop told me after his death that he always referred to me as his favourite author, which I regard as a singular compliment.

Later

There has been great controversy since Burns's death about his character. In my opinion, on his arrival in Edinburgh for the first time he was essentially virtuous – he had what I would describe as the light of genius – but he was seduced by dissipated companions, and after his move to Dumfriesshire, he allowed himself to fall into drunkenness. Although in the later years he occasionally produced work of merit, his addiction to alcohol got the better of him and consigned him to an early grave.

It is claimed that Burns was an independent thinker. That I do not accept. He had independence in his mouth more than in his mind. His idea of independence was a love of licentiousness and contempt for order, whereas true independence of thought involves a love of virtue and contempt for vice.

CHAPTER 8

THE TOURS

1787

ROBERT AINSLIE

Robert Ainslie was about to celebrate his twenty-first birthday
in December 1786 when John Richmond introduced him to
Robert Burns. At the time, Ainslie was studying to become a
lawyer as an apprentice to Samuel Mitchelson in Carrubber's
Close, Edinburgh. He completed his studies and was admitted
as a Writer to the Signet on 9th July 1789. He was introduced to
Mrs Agnes McLehose by Burns, and when Burns moved to
Dumfries, Ainslie became her adviser and close confidant. After
Burns died, he acted for Mrs McLehose in recovering her letters
to Burns from the Committee of Trustees.

He was invited to join the Committee promoting the Burns
Mausoleum in 1814 but declined to participate. His affairs took
a turn for the worse in later life and he suffered the indignity of
being sequestrated on 12th March 1821. His creditors received
a dividend of two shillings in the pound and he received a
Discharge on 28th July 1821.

Ainslie became an author of books of a religious nature,
including *Essays on the Evidence of Christianity.*

My name is Robert Ainslie. I am a lawyer and writer. I am forty years of age. I make this statement on 31st March 1806.

I had become acquainted with John Richmond, Robert Burns's friend, in the latter part of 1785 when he arrived in Edinburgh from Ayrshire to a new position as a legal clerk in the employment of William Wilson of Howden, an elderly Writer to the Signet. At the time, Wilson's son – also called William – was an apprentice in the firm. John and young William never got on, and when Wilson Senior died in June 1787, John moved back to Ayrshire. At the time, I was in practice as a lawyer on my own account, having completed my apprenticeship with Samuel Mitchelson.

John and I were more or less contemporaries, and we socialised together. John was excited when he learned that Robert was journeying to Edinburgh to promote a second edition of his poetry. John had loaned me his copy of the Kilmarnock Edition, so I was familiar with Robert's work.

Robert arrived in Edinburgh already replete with patronage. He was welcomed to our Masonic Lodge and introduced to many brother Freemasons who could potentially help with his work. In no time at all he had agreements with William Creech, William Smellie and William Scott covering the publication, printing and binding of his first Edinburgh Edition, which appeared at the beginning of April 1787.

Throughout our friendship, Robert asked me for my views on the various legal issues he had to deal with, and the counsel he was being given. He trusted Henry Mackenzie who advised in his negotiations with Creech, though I was never sure whom Mackenzie was acting for.

Robert and John used to entertain me with their tales of life in Mauchline, and in particular their 'Court of Equity'. I have to say, they made light of certain matters in a way that might to others have been seen as hypocritical bearing in mind that both had fathered illegitimate children. They both continued their adventures with the fairer sex with enthusiasm while in Edinburgh.

At the beginning of May, about a week after the appearance of the first Edinburgh Edition, Robert and I embarked on a tour of the Borders. We first journeyed to Haddington and Gifford, then south to my parents' home Berrywell, near Duns. We attended the church service at Duns with my sister Rachel, and the minister's sermon referred to a paragraph of scripture which denounced obstinate sinners. My sister was leafing through her Bible in search of the paragraph when Robert scribbled out a verse[1] and passed it to her:

> Fair maid, you need not take the hint,
> Nor idle texts pursue:
> 'Twas guilty sinners that he meant,
> Not Angels such as you!

This demonstrated Robert's quick-wittedness, though I kept a careful eye on my sister and him until we left Berrywell!

Thereafter, we criss-crossed the area, visiting Coldstream, Kelso, Melrose and Innerleithen. I had but two weeks of holiday, so I had to return to Edinburgh after we were made Royal Arch Masons at the Lodge St Ebbe in Eyemouth on Saturday 19th May. As can be seen from the Lodge Minute,[2] Robert was the star of the evening:

EYEMOUTH, 19th May 1787

> At a general encampment held this day, the following brethren were made Royal Arch Masons – namely, Robert Burns, from the Lodge of St James's, Tarbolton, Ayrshire, and Robert Ainslie, from the Lodge of St Luke's, Edinburgh, by James Carmichael,

Wm. Grieve, Daniel Dow, John Clay, Robert Grieve etc. etc. Robert Ainslie paid one guinea admission dues; but on account of R. Burns's remarkable poetical genius, the encampment unanimously agreed to admit him gratis, and considered themselves honoured by having a man of such shining abilities for one of their companions.

Robert continued on his tour with other friends through the north of England. He wrote to me from Newcastle, making it clear his new companions were of a more serious disposition than I was. He then fell foul of the local bye-laws in Carlisle by riding his horse (which he had named Jenny Geddes in what I thought at the time a somewhat puerile gesture) in a municipal park, but the magistrate imposed no penalty for fear Robert might compose a verse lampooning him.

At the beginning of June, Robert was in Dumfries and received the Freedom of the burgh. It was while he was there that he received the first intimation of another aberration which was to haunt him. In April, while in Edinburgh, Robert had seduced a servant, and the girl, called Margaret Cameron, now claimed to be pregnant by him. Robert sent me a letter[3] about her from Dumfries at the beginning of June in the following terms:

My Dear friend

My first welcome to this place was the inclosed letter. – I am very sorry for it, but what is done is done – I pay you no compliment when I say that except my old friend Smith there is not any person in the world I would trust so far.– Please call at the James Hog mentioned, and send for the wench and give her Ten or Twelve Shillings, but don't for Heaven's sake meddle with her as a Piece. – I insist on this, on your honor;

and advise her out to some country friends.– You may perhaps not like the business, but I just tax your friendship thus far. – Call for God's sake, lest the poor soul be starving. Ask her for a letter I wrote her just now, by way of token. It is unsigned. – Write me after the meeting.

Dumfries, June 1787   Robt. Burns

This was irony indeed, in that I myself was in the same position as Robert. A servant girl, with whom I had 'meddled with as a piece', was expecting my child, and I was having to face up to making some financial arrangement with her. In fact, I was able to seek out Margaret Cameron and found she was indeed in a distressed state, but at that stage she had been advised to start a court action against Robert, and was not amenable to any financial settlement. Robert was later served with a writ in the following terms:[4]

UNTO THE SHERIFF OF THE COUNTY OF MIDLOTHIAN
PETITION
of
MARGARET CAMERON, a resident of Edinburgh,
PETITIONER
for
Warrant to apprehend ROBERT BURNS, Poet in Edinburgh

HUMBLY SHEWETH:-

(One)   That the Petitioner, Margaret Cameron, is pregnant to the said Robert Burns in consequence of sexual connection which took place between them.

(Two)   That the Petitioner has been credibly informed, and in her conscience believes, that the said Robert Burns is presently in meditatione fugae and about to leave Scotland in order to avoid the Petitioner's lawful claim against him for inlying expenses, and aliment to the child; and

(Three)   That the Petitioner will thereby be defrauded or disappointed of her claim against the said Robert Burns for such inlying expenses and aliment.

> **MAY IT THEREFORE** please your Lordship to take the Petitioner's oath to the verity of the statements made in this Petition; and thereon to grant warrant to apprehend and bring the said Robert Burns before your Lordship for examination; and thereafter to commit him to the prison of Edinburgh, therein to be detained until he finds sufficient caution, acted in your Lordship's Court Books, de judicio sisti in any action for payment of the said inlying expenses and aliment, and consequents, which may be raised against him, at the instance of the Petitioner; and in case the said Robert Burns has left or may leave your Lordship's jurisdiction, to recommend to all other Judges and Magistrates to concur in your Lordship's said warrant And in the event of opposition to find the said Robert Burns liable in expenses, and to decern therefor.
>
> According to Justice, &c.

While in Dumfries Robert found the people he met most agreeable. As was his wont, he was most attracted to the females, and joked that he almost broke the Tenth Commandment on account of the local clergyman's wife, a Mrs Anne Burnside.

On leaving Dumfries Robert took the opportunity to look over the Dalswinton Estate owned by our brother Freemason Patrick Miller, who had suggested Robert lease one of his farms. He then returned to Mauchline.

There, he found the attitude of the Armour family towards him had completely changed. Contempt had been transformed to adulation. This did not go down well with Robert at the time. He wrote that if anything had been wanting to disgust him completely at Armour's family, their mean, servile compliance now would have done it.

Robert then set out alone on a short tour of the West Highlands. He wrote a brief note to me about his tour from Arrochar on 25th June. In this letter, he voiced doubts about whether he was really the father of the child being carried by Margaret Cameron. He did not pursue that, however. I know he then journeyed to Dumbarton, where he was made a Burgess and Guild Brother of the Burgh on 29th June; he also took the opportunity to collect subscriptions due by the many local Freemasons who had subscribed to the first Edinburgh Edition.

I next heard from him in July by way of a letter[5] which I still treasure:

My Dear Ainslie

There is one thing for which I set great store by you as a friend, and it is this, that I have not a friend upon earth, besides yourself, to whom I can talk nonsense without forfeiting some degree of his esteem. Now, to one like me, who never cares for speaking any thing else but nonsense, such a friend as you is an invaluable treasure. I was never a rogue, but have been a fool all my life; and, in spite of all my endeavours, I see now plainly that I shall never be wise. Now it rejoices my heart to have met with such a fellow as you, who, though you are not just such a hopeless fool as I, yet I trust you will never listen so much to the temptations of the devil as to grow so very wise that you will in the least disrespect an honest fellow because he is a fool. In short, I have set you down as the staff of my old age, when the whole list of my friends will, after a decent share of pity, have forgot me.

> Though in the morn comes start and strife,
> Yet joy may come at noon;
> And I hope to live a merry merry life
> When a' thir days are done.

Write me soon, were it but a few lines, just to tell me how that good, sagacious man your father is,–that kind, dainty body your mother,–that strapping chiel your brother Douglas–and my friend Rachel, who is as far before Rachel of old, as she was before her blear-eyed sister Leah.

Mauchline, 23rd July 1787   R.B.

I replied to this letter, taking the opportunity to let him know that my servant girl had produced my illegitimate son. That prompted a letter dated 29th July from Robert, and the following excerpt[6] betrays his rather unrealistic view of life:

THE TOURS

My Dear Ainslie

Give you joy, give you joy, My dear brother! may your child be as strong a man as Samson, as wise a man as Solomon, & as honest a man as his father.–I have double health & spirits at the news.–Welcome, Sir, to the society, the venerable Society, of FATHERS!!!

> Lord's children are God's heritage;
> The womb's fruit his reward;
> The sons of youth as arrows are
> In strong men's hands prepar'd.
>
> O, happy is the man that hath
> His quiver fill'd with those!
> He unashamed in the gate
> Shall speak unto his foes!

But truce, with the Psalmist! I shall certainly give you a congratulatory Poem on the birth day myself. My ailing child is got better, and the Mother is certainly in for it again, and Peggy will bring a gallant half-Highlander, and I shall get a farm, and keep them all about my hand, and breed them in the fear of the Lord and an oakstick, and I shall be the happiest man upon earth.

A letter I just now got from Creech's oblidges me to be in Edinburgh again this day, or tomorrow's e'en night, and then what a shaking of hands, and what coveys of good things, between you & I, I will call for you at Mitchelson's the moment I arrive.

Writing Sense is so damn'd, dry, hide-bound a business, I am determined never more to have any thing to do with it. I have such an aversion to right line and method, that when I can't get over the hedges which bound the highway, I zig-zag across the road just to keep my hand in. I am just now going to church, and will remember you in my prayers.– Farewell!

Mauchline, 29th. July 1787   Robt. Burns

How he ever thought he could establish such a ménage of children by different mothers was beyond me. He became ever more fanciful in a letter to me at the end of August, advising me to give my son a scriptural name such as Zimri or Achithophel, but using Burns as his middle name. I did not take up his suggestion.

In the middle of August, Robert had to deal with settling the action brought against him by Margaret Cameron. He found sufficient to pay her off and the case was dropped. I have no idea what happened to the child.

At this time Robert had rooms in the house of William Nicol, Classics Master at the High School of Edinburgh. Nicol was a most unusual character. He came from humble beginnings just like Robert – his father was a tailor – but he was a brilliant scholar and had studied divinity, medicine and Classics at the University of Edinburgh. Their mutual acquaintance, Alexander Young of Harben, who was Nicol's lawyer, regarded Nicol as possessing intellect superior to Robert's. Nicol was, however, highly opinionated, argumentative, short-tempered, pedantic, and did not suffer fools gladly. He also had Jacobite sympathies. Robert loved his verbal jousts with Nicol, but frequently found himself embarrassed by his friend when in company with strangers.

Nicol was fifteen years older than Robert, so when they decided to embark on a tour of the Highlands in August they elected to hire a post-chaise rather than proceed on horseback. In Linlithgow Robert was made an honorary member of Lodge Linlithgow Ancient Brazen, and when the pair were at Stirling Castle, Nicol was able to give vent to his feelings of despair at seeing the ruined state of the great hall where Scottish Parliaments had met. That inspired Robert to etch the following verses[7] on a window at the inn where they were staying:

> Here Stuarts once in glory reigned,
> And laws for Scotland's weal ordained;
> But now unroof'd their palace stands,
> Their sceptre's sway'd by other hands;
> Fallen indeed, and to the earth
> Whence grovelling reptiles take their birth,
> The injured Stuart line is gone,
> A race outlandish fills the throne;
> An idiot race, to honour lost;
> Who know them best despise them most.

This would not be the last time that Robert's sentimental view of history and his naïvity in criticising the House of Hanover would haunt him. On a later visit to Stirling he destroyed the etching, but by then the damage had been done as copies had been widely circulated. I do know that the terms of that etching almost prevented Burns being allowed to apply for a post as a gauger with the Excise.

George Hamilton was the son of John Hamilton, the Minister at Bolton. He originally intended to practise as a barrister, and was entered at the Inner Temple. He took exception to what Burns had written, and composed a reply[8] in the following terms:

> Thus wretches rail whom sordid gain
> Drags in Faction's gilded chain;
> But can a mind which Fame inspires,
> Where genius lights her brightest fires—
> Can BURNS, disdaining truth and law,
> Faction's venomed dagger draw;

> And, skulking with a villain's aim,
> Basely stab his monarch's fame?
> Yes, Burns, 'tie o'er, thy race is run,
> And shades receive thy setting sun
> With pain thy wayward fate I see,
> And mourn the lot that's doomed for thee:
> These few rash lines will damn thy name,
> And blast thy hopes of future fame.

Later, Robert responded to what he described as the very petulant reply[9] to his imprudent lines.

> With Aesop's lion, Burns, says sore I feel
> Each other blow, but damn that ass's heel.

Robert took the opportunity during this tour to visit Gavin Hamilton's relations at Harvieston, near Dollar. He reported the visit to Gavin, as he put it, not to flatter him but to reproach him for failing to keep up his correspondence with his family. Robert described Gavin's half-sister Charlotte in particularly complimentary terms, but she was merely the latest to receive such an accolade, after my sister and the Minister's wife in Dumfries!

The tour took Nicol and Robert to North-East Scotland for three weeks. Robert anticipated that Nicol might be a difficult travelling companion – he later described the trip as being akin to travelling with a loaded blunderbuss at full cock – and Nicol lived up to his reputation. On two occasions, his impatience required Robert to decline invitations from hosts whose company he enjoyed.

Robert had a letter of introduction to the Duke of Atholl, and at Castle Blair, where Robert's friend Josiah Walker was engaged as a tutor to the children. Josiah arranged to meet Robert and Nicol at a local inn, and conveyed an invitation to Robert to stay at the Castle.

Unfortunately, the invitation was not extended to Nicol, so he had to put up at the inn. Another house guest at the Castle was Robert Graham of Fintry who had shortly beforehand been appointed a Commissioner of the Scottish Board of Excise. Graham was later to feature in Robert's appointment to and travails in the Excise. Nicol felt slighted by the lack of an invitation to stay at the Castle, and prevailed upon Robert to leave after a couple of days. Had Robert stayed another day, he would have met Henry Dundas, William Pitt's placeman ruler of Scotland, who had already featured in some of Robert's satires. I have often wondered whether Dundas might have warmed to Robert, and offered him a sinecure. However, the two never met, and Robert's antipathy towards Dundas intensified over the years.

A similar situation arose later in the tour. Robert had been invited to dinner at Castle Gordon, and when the Duke and Duchess of Gordon realised that Nicol was accompanying Robert, they extended an invitation to him. Now Nicol regarded their tardiness in issuing the invitation, rather than the lack of one, as a slight, flew into a rage, and insisted that Robert proceed on the journey with him forthwith, leaving the Duke and Duchess and their guests somewhat bemused.

In the latter part of the tour Robert met relatives in Stonehaven and spent time with his cousin James Burness in Montrose.

After he returned to Edinburgh I think Robert had had enough of Nicol; he described him as 'that obstinate Son of Latin Prose', and in October he found new lodgings in St James's Square with William Cruikshank, a fellow master of Nicol's at the High School. Coincidentally, I myself had moved to a property in the same square around that time.

Robert was hoping to finalise arrangements with Creech but after two weeks or so he decided to embark on another tour. His companion was his Ayrshire friend Doctor James Adair, who had studied in Geneva and at the University of Edinburgh and at the time had a medical practice in Edinburgh. They visited the Carron Ironworks in Falkirk before proceeding to Stirling where they encountered a group of travellers from Edinburgh, including the redoubtable Nicol, and an evening of wine and song ensued. Adair and Robert then journeyed to Harvieston, where Adair was introduced to Charlotte Hamilton, previously admired by Robert. But it was to Adair that Charlotte directed her favours, and she and Adair were married two years later. During his eight-day stay at Harvieston, Robert renewed his friendship with Peggy Chalmers, a niece of Gavin Hamilton's stepmother. Robert regarded Peggy Chalmers as his intellectual equal, and so enjoyed her company that he later said he had lived more of real life with her in eight days than he could do with anyone else in eight years.

Shortly after his return to Edinburgh, Robert received distressing news. For some reason, the care of Robert's twins, young Robert and Jean, had been split between Jean's family in Mauchline and Gilbert's at Mossgiel. While Robert was in Edinburgh, his daughter Jean died; she was just over a year old. Gilbert told me later that he was horrified that Robert did not come to comfort the child's mother in her loss. Robert never spoke much about the loss of young Jean. He knew at the time that the child's mother was once again pregnant by him, and from his earlier letter to me in August it can be seen that he contemplated a kind of fresh start at a new farm with all his family. He was, however, determined not to leave Edinburgh again until he had wound up matters with Creech, which he described as a tedious business.

The possible lease of Patrick Miller's farm at Ellisland, and what then was the alternative of joining the Excise, were matters which preyed on his mind at this time, but the main subject of his worry in that period was Creech. As might have been anticipated, Creech was dilatory in settling up with Robert. Indeed, it was only on 23rd October that Robert received Creech's Promissory Note:[10]

Edinburgh, Oct. 23rd 1787.

On demand I promise to pay Mr Robert Burns, or Order, One Hundred Guineas, value received.

William Creech

This was in exchange for an Assignation[11] by Robert in his favour:

I, Robert Burns, late in Mossgiel, Parish of Mauchline, Ayrshire, presently residing in Edinburgh, hereby Convey and Make over to William Creech, Bookseller in Edinburgh, his heirs or assignees the sole property legally inherent in me of Poems already published by me in One Volume Octavo, and of which I am the Author, with any additions, alterations, or corrections which I may make to the said Volume in any future Edition if such shall be, upon the consideration of the said William Creech paying to me, my heirs or assignees, the sum of One hundred Guineas, for which sum he has presently given me security and satisfaction. – In Witness Whereof I have subscribed these presents written on stamped paper by Robert Cameron, Writer in Edinburgh, at Edinburgh the Twenty third day of October, One Thousand Seven Hundred and Eighty Seven years before these witnesses Peter Hill, clerk to the said William Creech and the said Robert Cameron –

Peter Hill, Witness

Robt Burns

R Cameron, Witness

Creech continued to fob Robert off with excuses even after granting the Note, but Robert was to some extent reassured by its receipt. He threw himself into developing his collaboration with our brother Freemason James Johnson, the engraver in Edinburgh, producing collections of native Scots songs and setting them to music. The first volume of *The Scots Musical Museum* had been published by Johnson in May, and a second volume was scheduled for publication in March 1788.

Poor health had laid Robert low on a few occasions since his arrival in Edinburgh, and this continued, as can be seen from his letter[12] to me at the end of November:

> I beg, my dear Sir, you would not make any appointment to take us to Ainslie's tonight. On looking over my engagements, constitution, present state of my health, some little vexatious soul concerns, &c. I find I can't sup abroad tonight.
>
> I shall be in today till one o'clock if you have a leisure hour, &c.
>
> You will think it romantic when I tell you that I find the idea of your friendship almost necessary to my existence.–You assume a proper length of face in my bitter hours of blue-devilism, and you laugh fully up to my highest wishes at my good things.–I don't know upon the whole, if you are one of the first fellows in God's world, but you are so to me.–I tell you this just now in the conviction that some inequalities in my temper and manner may perhaps sometimes make you suspect that I am not so warmly as I ought to be.
>
> Your friend,
>
> Sunday morn. Robt. Burns

I know that at the beginning of December Robert met Mrs Agnes McLehose for the first time. She was twenty-eight years old, the estranged wife of James McLehose, a Glasgow lawyer whom she had married against the wishes of her family at the age of seventeen. Her father was an eminent surgeon in Glasgow and, after leaving her husband because of his behaviour, she had returned to the family home in Glasgow with their three children. After the death of her father she had moved to Edinburgh to a house in Potterrow. I suspect that was because her cousin William Craig (later the Court of Session judge, Lord Craig) was in practice in Edinburgh as a successful advocate. I later learned that Craig generously supplemented his cousin's trust income to support her lifestyle.

Robert met Mrs McLehose at a tea party and they became infatuated with one another. Robert would talk of little else for days on end, even while he was incapacitated following a fall. Eventually, I was introduced to her. I must say I found her a somewhat overpowering lady – at the time I was only twenty-one, and I was at a loss to understand why Robert got so wound up about their affair, if that is what it was. My opinion of her changed over the years, though, and I became very friendly with her and her family. I later engaged her son Andrew as an apprentice in my legal practice.

Robert was ill advised to attend the Jacobite Club in Edinburgh on 31st December 1787 to celebrate the birthday of Charles Edward Stuart, the Young Pretender to the throne who lived in exile in France, and, more seriously, to compose 'A Birthday Ode' containing what were clearly radical sentiments. It is a clear example of Robert's lack of judgment in writing something to please his audience. Sadly, this was a recurring fault.

I like to think that between 1786 and 1790, Robert and I were very close friends. Later we grew apart.

Later

Robert and I continued to correspond when he took on Ellisland. I dealt as best I could with Mrs McLehose's maidservant Jenny Clow who approached me in 1788 seeking damages and expenses when she discovered she was carrying Robert's child, eventually reaching a settlement with her.

Doubts were expressed by Robert about the financial viability of Ellisland from an early stage. In 1789, when he wrote congratulating me on my being admitted as a Writer to the Signet, he explained that while he was unhappy about the work he was doing as an exciseman, he was pleased to be continuing to contribute to Johnson's *The Scots Musical Museum*. He did say that he was earning £70 annually.

I visited him at Ellisland in October 1790, when I found him greatly changed, transformed from an Edinburgh beau to a gritty rustic.

Our last correspondence was in 1793, and when I received his letter of 26th April that year, in which he called himself 'Spunkie', I began to have doubts about his mental state. By that time I was a close confidant of Mrs McLehose, in whose interests I subsequently acted following Robert's death. I make no apology for that. I later became estranged from her, however.

It is interesting that George Hamilton featured again in Robert's life. George received the call to the ministry, and became the Minister at Gladsmuir in 1790. He is the Moderator of the Church of Scotland at the present time. In 1796 he composed the epistle to Robert's friend Harry Erskine, purportedly from the banished republican Thomas Muir, which I am told greatly amused Robert.

CHAPTER 9

A JUDGMENT

EARLY 1788

SIR THOMAS MILLER,
LORD PRESIDENT GLENLEE

Born in 1717, Thomas Miller was educated at the University of Glasgow and became an Advocate in 1742. Miller was Sheriff of Kirkcudbright from 1748 to 1754 and was Solicitor of the Excise in Scotland from 1755. He was appointed Solicitor General for Scotland in 1759, and promoted to Lord Advocate in 1760.

He served as Member of Parliament for Dumfries Burghs from 1761 until appointed Lord Justice Clerk in 1766, taking the judicial title 'Lord Barskimming'. In 1788, he became Lord President of the Court of Session, the most senior judge in Scotland, with the title 'Lord Glenlee'. He died a year later.

My name is Thomas Miller. I am Lord President of the Court of Session, with the judicial title Lord Glenlee. I am seventy-two years of age. I make this statement on 30th June 1789.

I was an early admirer of Robert Burns, mostly through local knowledge. My country estate is close to Mauchline, so I became aware of his talent from my friends in the legal profession in Ayrshire. I believe Burns is referring to me in this verse from his poem 'The Vision'[1] (and I take that to be a compliment):

> Thro' many a wild, romantic grove,
> Near many a hermit-fancied cove
> (Fit haunts for friendship or for love,
> In musing mood),
> An aged Judge, I saw him rove,
> Dispensing good.

Of course, I know all about what could be described as the unsavoury side of Burns's character. He is responsible for a number of bastard children, although it is to his credit that he has provided for all of them, if the rumours to that effect are correct.

When Burns arrived in Edinburgh in 1786, he took the literary cognoscenti by storm. I am more hesitant than most of my fellow judges in lauding 'the ploughman poet' and his brother Gilbert for two reasons. Firstly, I know all about their background, and, in particular, their father William's long-running dispute with his landlord, David McClure, which I have discussed on a number of occasions with Lord Swinton. I take a dim view of the delaying tactics the family employed, their secret flitting to Gavin Hamilton's farm, and the evasion of their liabilities to William Burnes's creditors. Secondly, and more importantly, so far as the poet himself is concerned, my rather eccentric brother Patrick has offered Burns the lease of part of his estate near Dumfries, a proposition which I view with consternation and trepidation in view of the Burns family's farming record.

Perhaps I am being unfair in describing my brother Patrick as an eccentric; he is more of a polymath. He has had a long-standing interest in nautical engineering and, recently, a successful trial was held on Dalswinton Loch on his Dumfries estate of a twin-hulled steam-driven boat. Patrick is also a high-regarded businessman. He is a director of both the Carron Engineering Company and the Bank of Scotland. My main concern is that he bought the main part of Dalswinton Estate in 1785 with no clear idea of how he was going to manage it, and he compounded that in 1786 by buying more adjoining land – Ellisland Farm – from my fellow Court of Session judge Lord Elliock.

My brother first met Burns at Lodge Canongate Kilwinning when the poet arrived in Edinburgh, and Patrick became determined to assist him in every way. Burns had been a Depute Master in Tarbolton and was admitted to Lodge Canongate Kilwinning in February 1787.

I was persuaded by Patrick to become a subscriber to the Edinburgh Edition of Burns's poems which was published by William Creech in 1787. I still enjoy reading 'The Twa Dugs'.

Patrick frequently discusses business matters with me, so I am aware that there was a period when it looked far from certain that Burns would become his tenant at Dalswinton, for Burns was at that time considering a career in the Excise. It was around this time that several incidents were reported to me by friends and colleagues which caused me to counsel my brother to be cautious in his dealings with Burns. I know that William Creech holds back in settling up with all his creditors to the last possible moment, and that Burns had become more and more agitated about his publisher's delaying tactics in avoiding settling both the subscription money and money due under his Promissory Note. I am told Burns was recently intercepted by a friend in Leith Walk, the poet purple with rage, somewhat the worse for wear, brandishing a stout stick and shouting at the top of his voice, "I am going to smash that shite Creech."[2]

I then heard that in March, Jean Armour, who may be described as Burns's inamorata of long standing, the mother of his first set of twins, had produced yet another set by him, but both had died within the week. Burns appeared totally unaffected by this, and made no effort to return to Ayrshire to attend their funerals or to comfort the mother.

But the major matter of concern to me is Burns's relationship with Mrs Agnes McLehose, cousin of the senior advocate William Craig. Burns was apparently conducting a clandestine affair with this previously respectable married woman in the first quarter of the year, at the same time as Jean Armour was producing his twins, and he was swithering between a career in the Excise and becoming my brother's tenant. I know that he tried to enlist the help of James Cunningham, the Earl of Glencairn, in using his influence to procure him a grant from the Commissioners of Excise, citing the need to save the little home that sheltered an aged mother, two brothers and three sisters from destruction. This was pathetic. Of course, it has later transpired that while all this was going on, he seduced Jenny Clow, Mrs McLehose's maid, and yet another bastard child was born nine months later. This behaviour is utterly disgraceful.

Patrick, however, has chosen to ignore my advice, and has concluded a bargain with Burns. I do know that Burns inspected the Ellisland Farm at Dalswinton with farming friends on a number of occasions before completing the lease in March, so if it turns out to be a bad bargain for him, in the way of all previous Burns family farming enterprises, he has only himself to blame. I have a letter[3]

Burns wrote to my brother on 16th March last year which makes it clear that he knew what he was doing:

Sir

I send you Mr Gordon's scroll, and another which a professional man, a friend of mine, has done today.– This last is, I think, more distinctly what we have mutually agreed on; particularly the 300L .–According to your idea, I have mentioned applying the surplus, if any be, to the improvement of the land; and as I told you, I wish to keep 50L of the first recd monies, to be the latest accounted for, in case my stock be rather scanty.–There is some fishing rights the present tenant possesses; if you intend that I should enjoy the same, it will be best, I suppose, to mention it in the tack; if you do not understand that I am to have that priviledge, 'tis but a trifling matter, and I don't much care.–If this scroll meets your approbation, I shall wait on Mr Gordon to get the tack extended, so soon as you return me the papers.–

> I have the honor to be ever,
> Sir,
> your highly oblidged and
> most respectful humble Servt.

St Jas' Sqr, Sunday even.   Robt. Burns

A few days later, he and Patrick signed the lease.[4] In summary, Burns is leasing Ellisland for a total of seventy-six years at an annual rent of £70, reduced in the first three years to £50, and Patrick is to contribute £300 towards the building of a new farmhouse and other improvements.

I am not sure how well Burns is managing Ellisland. Patrick speaks seldom about the estate, other than to say that the farm buildings are being erected, and Burns is combining his life as a farmer with that of an excise officer. His relationship with Mrs McLehose appears to have foundered, perhaps on account of the distance between them.

CHAPTER 10

WHIGS AND TORIES

1788

HENRY (HARRY) ERSKINE

Harry Erskine was admitted to the Faculty of Advocates on 23rd February 1768 and served two periods as Lord Advocate, from 1783 to 1784 and from 1806 to 1807. He was elected Dean of the Faculty of Advocates in 1785.

He was a Whig sympathiser and an advocate of parliamentary reform. Owing to his involvement with the reform movement, he was voted out of office as Dean of Faculty in 1795. He retired from practice in 1811 and died in 1817.

My name is Harry Erskine. I am fifty-nine years of age. I make this statement on 31st March 1806.

I met Robert Burns at a meeting of Lodge Canongate Kilwinning. I was a past Right Worshipful Master of the Lodge, but in 1781 I had to stand down from that high office as it was incompatible with my practice at the Court of Session.

I had read some of Burns's poetry from his Kilmarnock edition prior to his arrival in Edinburgh late in 1786. Shortly after I met him for the first time in December that year, he sent me the following letter:[1]

> Sir
>
> I shewed the inclosed political ballad to my Lord Glencairn, to have his opinion whether I should publish it; as I suspect my political tenets, such as they are, may be rather heretical in the opinion of some of my best friends.–I have a few first principles in religion and politics which, I believe, I would not easily part with; but for all the etiquette of, by whom, in what manner, &c. I would not have a dissocial word about it with any one of God's creatures; particularly, an honored patron, or a respected friend.–His Lordship seems to think the piece may appear in print, but desired me to send you a copy for your suffrage.–I am, with the sincerest gratitude for the notice with which you have been pleased to honor the rustic bard, sir, your most devoted humble servant,
>
> Two o' clock   Robt. Burns

The poem he enclosed was his 'Ballad on the American War':[2]

When Guilford good our Pilot stood,
An' did our hellim thraw, man,
Ae night, at tea, began a plea
Within America, man:
Then up they gat the maskin-pat,
And in the sea did jaw, man;
An' did nae less, in full Congress,
Than quite refuse our law, man.

Then thro' the lakes Montgomery takes,
I wat he was na slaw, man;
Down Lowrie's Burn he took a turn,
And Carleton did ca', man:
But yet, whatreck, he, at Quebec,
Montgomery – like did fa', man,
Wi' sword in hand, before his band,
Amang his en'mies a', man.

Poor Tammy Gage within a cage
Was kept at Boston-ha', man,
Till Willie Howe took o'er the knowe
For Philadelphia, man;
Wi' sword an' gun he thought a sin
Guid Christian bluid to draw, man;
But at New York, wi' knife an' fork,
Sir Loin he hacked sma', man.

Burgoyne gaed up, like spur an' whip,
Till Fraser brave did fa', man;
Then lost his way, ae misty day,
In Saratoga shaw, man.
Cornwallis fought as lang's he dought,
An' did the Buckskins claw, man;
But Clinton's glaive, frae rust to save,
He hung it to the wa', man.

120

Then Montague, an' Guilford too,
Began to fear, a fa', man;
And Sackville doure, wha stood the stoure,
The German chief to thraw, man:
For Paddy Burke, like ony Turk,
Nae mercy had at a', man;
An' Charlie Fox threw by the box,
An' lows'd his tinkler jaw, man.

Then Rockingham took up the game,
Till Death did on him ca', man;
When Shelburne meek held up his cheek,
Conform to gospel law, man:
Saint Stephen's boys, wi' jarring noise,
They did his measures thraw, man,
For North an' Fox united stocks,
An' bore him to the wa', man.

Then Clubs an' Hearts were Charlie's cartes,
He swept the stakes awa', man,
Till the Diamond's Ace, of Indian race,
Led him a sair faux pas, man:
The Saxon lads, wi' loud placads,
On Chatham's Boy did ca', man,
An' Scotland drew her pipe an' blew,
"Up, Willie, waur them a', man!"

Behind the throne then Granville's gone,
A secret word or twa, man;
While slee Dundas arous'd the class
Be-north the Roman wa', man:
An' Chatham's wraith, in heav'nly graith,
(Inspired Bardies saw, man)
Wi' kindling eyes, cry'd, "Willie, rise!
Would I hae fear'd them a', man!'

But, word an' blow, North, Fox, and Co.
Gowff'd Willie like a ba', man,
Till Suthron raise, an' coost their claise
Behind him in a raw, man:
An' Caledon threw by the drone,
An' did her whittle draw, man;
An' swoor fu' rude, thro' dirt an' blood,
To mak it guid in law, man.

I agreed with Lord Glencairn that the poem was worthy of inclusion in the Edinburgh Edition. I have been criticised for that, and I will explain why I thought these nine verses have merit. I understand Burns composed the poem in 1784, just after the Treaty of Paris was signed, ending the American Revolutionary War.

Guilford is, of course, the late Lord North, who as Prime Minister from 1770 until 1782 had a major influence on events leading up to the War, and the conduct of the War itself. He was the first Tory to hold office as Prime Minister for decades.

The first four verses are a narrative of events during the war, from the imposition of excise duties on the colonists which actuated the Boston Tea Party, the Congress which led to the Declaration of Independence in 1776, and the subsequent military campaigns, culminating in the surrender by Cornwallis at Yorktown in 1781.

The other five verses are more provocative and daring, with their commentary on the political machinations in the two years following, including the scapegoating of Viscount Sackville, who had been Secretary of State for the Colonies, the appointment of the Whig Lord Rockingham as Prime Minister, and his death and replacement by another Whig, William Petty, Earl of Shelburne. William Pitt's great rival Whig, Charles Fox, then aligned with North to form a coalition, but that dissolved and King George III asked Pitt to form a government.

I have always been puzzled by the lack of regard for Burns's intelligence. What the above poem demonstrates is his grasp of history and his analytical talent, combining humour with sarcasm. I will admit that the reference to Henry Dundas as 'slee', meaning sly and calculating, caused widespread amusement among many of my Whig colleagues at the Faculty of Advocates. At the time, he was, of course, widely regarded as the political leader of Scotland, with unprecedented influence and power. He was also half-brother of the late Lord President Dundas the Younger, and I understand that the Lord President was not best pleased to read the poem shortly before his death. I was therefore amused to hear later of Burns's surprise when the Dundas family did not acknowledge a eulogy he composed after the death of the Lord President.

In 1787 Burns had composed an epigram, 'Extempore in the Court of Session',[3] which, I think, is somewhat over-complimentary of my style of advocacy. He compared me to the then Lord Advocate, Sir Ilay Campbell, now the Lord President:

LORD ADVOCATE

He clench'd his pamphlets in his fist,
He quoted and he hinted,
Till in a declamation-mist,
His argument he tint it:
He gaped for't, he graped for't,
He fand it was awa, man;
But what his common sense came short,
He eked out wi' law, man.

MR ERSKINE

Collected, Harry stood a wee,
Then open'd out his arm, man;

His Lordship sat wi' rueful e'e,
And ey'd the gathering storm, man;
Like wind-driv'n hail it did assail,
Or torrents o'er a lin, man;
The BENCH sae wise lift up their eyes,
Hauf-wauken'd wi' the din, man.

Burns was a guest at my home in Princes Street on many occasions in early 1788. He was an amusing and entertaining spirit at the dinner table. I know he was assisting James Johnson with the second edition of *The Scots Musical Museum*, his contributions including his 'Ballad on the American War'. But he was not in a state of contentment, and there was a darker and depressed side to him which he often revealed when we had discussions on our own. He was, however, making a supreme effort to be positive about the future.

After weeks of agonising, he finally settled on what he would do on leaving Edinburgh, by passing through the procedure to become part of the Excise, while also taking on the lease of part of Dalswinton Estate, which belonged to our brother Freemason Patrick Miller. On 7th April he sent a letter[4] from Mauchline to his Edinburgh lawyer friend William Dunbar, including the following:

> Sir
>
> ...
>
> I have been roving over the country, as the farm I have taken is forty miles from this place, hiring servants and preparing matters; but most of all, I am earnestly busy to bring about a revolution in my own mind. As, till within these eighteen months, I never was the wealthy master of ten guineas, my knowledge of business is to learn; add to this, my late scenes of idleness and dissipation have enervated my mind to an alarming

degree. Skill in the sober science of life is my most serious, and hourly study. I have dropt all conversation and all reading (prose reading) but what tends in some way or other to my serious aim. Except one worthy young fellow, I have not one single correspondent in Edinburgh. You have indeed kindly made me an offer of that kind. The world of wits, the *gens comme-il-faut* which I lately left, and with whom I never again will intimately mix–from that Port, Sir, I expect your Gazette: what *les beaux esprits* are saying, what they are doing, and what they are singing. Any sober intelligence from my sequestered walks of life; any droll original; any passing remark, important, forsooth, because it is mine; any little poetic effort, however embryoth; these, my dear sir, are all you have to expect from me...

> I am, My Dear Sir,
> ever most truly
> yours,

Mauchline, 7th April 1788   Robt. Burns

The 'worthy young fellow' was Robert Ainslie. I think one can sense Burns's bitterness and disillusion with his former Edinburgh admirers – including me – from this letter. His fame had indeed, for the moment, proved to be transient.

The late Lord President Glenlee has contributed his recollection of how Burns took on Ellisland. There were other farming issues troubling Robert at this time concerning his brother Gilbert and his lease of Mossgiel. Burns was now convinced that the Mossgiel lease was a wretched one, though he thought Gilbert would weather out the remaining seven years it had to run. With the benefit of hindsight, that was unduly pessimistic, for Gilbert remained at Mossgiel until

1798. John Richmond had tried to advise Burns and his brother on the proposal that they lease Mossgiel from the Mauchline writer Gavin Hamilton, but had been rebuffed. Now it seemed that Burns doubted the financial viability of Mossgiel. Things came to a head when Gavin Hamilton wrote to Burns asking him to guarantee a loan which his brother Gilbert needed. This excerpt, from his reply on 7th March 1788,[5] says it all:

> Sir
>
> The language of refusal is to me the most difficult language on earth, and you are the man of the world, excepting One of Rt Honble. designation, to whom it gives me the greatest pain to hold such language. My brother has already got money, and shall want nothing in my power to enable him to fulfil his engagement with you; but to be security on so large a scale, even for a brother, is what I dare not do, except I were in such circumstances of life as that the worst that might happen could not greatly injure me. I never wrote a letter which gave me so much pain in my life, as I know the unhappy consequences; I shall incur the displeasure of a Gentleman for whom I have the highest respect, and to whom I am deeply oblidged.
>
> I am ever, Sir,
> Your oblidged and very humble servt
>
> Mossgiel, Friday morn.   Robt. Burns

Burns's friendship with Gavin Hamilton cooled as a result of this, perhaps because Burns perceived that Hamilton was attempting to protect his own interests as Gilbert's landlord by procuring Burns as guarantor for Gilbert's debts. I know that Burns had already made a loan to his brother, which was still outstanding when Burns died.

Lord Glenlee has also referred to Burns's friendship with Mrs Agnes McLehose, and I know from her cousin William (now Lord Craig) that she and Burns were in almost constant touch by letter in the early part of 1788. Burns contributed a dedication to her entitled 'Clarinda, Mistress of my Soul' in the second edition of *The Scots Musical Museum*:[6]

> Clarinda, mistress of my soul,
> The measur'd time is run!
> The wretch beneath the dreary pole,
> So marks his latest sun.
>
> To what dark cave of frozen night
> Shall poor Sylvander hie;
> Depriv'd of thee, his life and light,
> The sun of all his joy.
>
> We part – but by these precious drops
> That fill thy lovely eyes!
> No other light shall guide my steps,
> Till thy bright beams arise.
>
> She, the fair sun of all her sex
> Has blest my glorious day;
> And shall a glimmering planet fix
> My worship to its ray?

Regular communication between them ceased when Burns left Edinburgh in March. I last saw Burns just before his departure; again, he was in a dark mood as a result of learning that one of the twins recently born to Jean Armour had died the day after her birth, and the other was dangerously ill. The other twin in fact died a few days later.

Bearing in mind how Burns had spoken to me about Jean Armour and the nature of his relationship with her, it came as a considerable surprise to me to learn at the end of May that Burns was referring to her as 'Mrs Burns'. His friend Robert Ainslie later explained to me that Burns had wanted to eliminate any doubt about the validity of his marriage, and that the Mauchline Church had recognised the marriage in the Session Minutes later in the year. According to Ainslie, Mrs McLehose did not take this news at all well.

Work at Ellisland started in June, and almost immediately Burns's correspondence betrayed a sense of foreboding that he might have made a mistake in taking on the lease there. His farm gave him a good many uncouth cares and anxieties, and he looked to employment by the Excise as a certainty of maintenance. Burns was calling in a number of favours from friends and acquaintances in order to smooth the way of his Excise commission, which he obtained in July after receiving a course of instruction in Ayrshire. Knowing what I did about how Burns shamelessly used his connections to obtain his Commission, it came as a considerable surprise to me to learn from Mrs Frances Dunlop that he had assured her that he had got the offer of the Excise without solicitation. According to Robert Graham of Fintry, Burns started sending pleading letters to him seeking preferential treatment in securing an appointment as an exciseman in the vicinity of Ellisland. I know that Graham found these letters to be a source of considerable embarrassment, particularly Burns's suggestion that the serving officer should be transferred or dismissed in order that Burns take over his post. At that stage, Graham was able to put Burns off.

Robert Ainslie had occasion to consult me about a delicate matter concerning Burns and Mrs McLehose, from which it was clear just how naïve in worldly matters 'Sylvander' and 'Clarinda' were. She had passed on some defamatory tittle-tattle about the High School Classics master William Nicol, another brother Freemason at Lodge Canongate Kilwinning. Nicol and Burns had toured the north of Scotland together and Burns had resided in Nicol's townhouse for a while. Very unwisely, Burns had repeated the remarks to William Cruikshank, another Master at the High School, speculating that the originator was Doctor Alexander Adam, the Rector of the High School. When a vicious litigation subsequently erupted between Adam and Nicol, the latter demanded that Burns reveal the identity of his informant, which Burns gallantly declined to do. There was then a threat that Burns would be cited as a witness, and it was on the issue of whether he could be compelled to give evidence that I was consulted. Fortunately I was able to influence Nicol indirectly to drop the matter in order to save Mrs McLehose embarrassment.

My defence that year of Deacon William Brodie, yet another brother Freemason of Burns and myself at Lodge Canongate Kilwinning, is only an interesting aside in my narrative of 1788, although there is a link in the story with Burns. The circumstances of Brodie's fall from grace are well known. Although outwardly a respectable businessman and public servant, he was part of a gang which carried out armed robberies in Edinburgh. He fled to Holland but was captured and returned for trial in Edinburgh. As a Freemason he brought shame on our Lodge.

The Lord Justice Clerk, Lord Braxfield, sat with Lords Hailes, Eskgrove, Swinton and Stonefield in judgment at the trial, where Brodie and his co-conspirator William Smith stood accused of robbing the Excise Office in Edinburgh. One of the witnesses for the prosecution was William Corbet, a Supervisor-General of the Excise. Corbet was a friend of Brodie and it was alleged that Brodie often accompanied him on visits to the Office and had made spurious visits there, allegedly to see Corbet, but in reality for the purpose of planning the robbery which later took place.

As was the practice, Lord Braxfield chose the fifteen male members of the jury. Somewhat remarkably, the assize included Burns's publisher William Creech and printer William Smellie, all members of our Lodge. Creech was selected as a juror and produced an account of the trial within a week of its conclusion.

The Crown prosecution was led by Ilay Campbell. I acted for Brodie, assisted by Charles Hay. Smith was represented by John Clerk and Robert Hamilton.

In his account, Creech describes my closing address to the jury as truly able and eloquent, displaying acuteness and ingenuity. Despite this and the efforts of the other defence counsel, both accused were unanimously convicted. On 1st October, both were executed before a crowd of about forty thousand.

It is clear that within a very short time of taking entry to his leased farm, Burns was concerned about the financial viability of the undertaking. I know he wrote to his friend Peggy Chalmers in September advising that he had his Excise commission in his pocket to save himself from the horrid situation of going down in a losing bargain to a farm, but by late 1788 Burns seemed to be content that his move to the Dumfries area would be a permanent one, for on 27th December he was admitted as a member of Lodge St Andrew Dumfries. The minute,[7] a copy of which was sent to my Lodge out of courtesy, was in the following terms:

> The Brethern having celebrated the Aniversary of St
> John in the usual manner, and Brother Robert Burns
> in Alliesland of St David's Strabolton, Lodge No. 178,
> being present, the Lodge unanimously assumed him a

Member of the Lodge, being a Master Masson, and he subscribed the regulations as a Member.

Masonic connections are, of course, always useful to someone setting up a new business in a new area.

Later

William Corbet, witness at Deacon Brodie's trial, was of great assistance to Burns in promoting him in the Excise. His wife and Burns's patron, Mrs Frances Dunlop, were close friends.

CHAPTER 11

REVOLUTIONS

1789

ALEXANDER FERGUSSON OF CRAIGDARROCH

Alexander Fergusson was admitted to the Faculty of Advocates in 1768 and was appointed Advocate Depute in 1783.

He was one of the most prominent and distinguished Freemasons of his day. He was elected Master of Lodge Canongate Kilwinning in 1784 and was Provincial Grand Master for the Southern District of Scotland from 1785. He was also a Justice of the Peace for Dumfries.

He could be described as a bon viveur, and was victor in a drinking contest in 1789 at Friar's Carse, the house of his cousin Captain Robert Riddell, when it was alleged that he had drunk upwards of five bottles of claret.

He was killed by the overturning of his carriage on the road from Dumfries to Craigdarroch in April 1796.

My name is Alexander Fergusson. I am a landowner and an advocate. I am forty-nine years of age. I make this statement on 31st March 1796.

I am the sixteenth Laird of Craigdarroch, near Moniaive, about thirty miles distant from Dumfries. My grandfather, the fourteenth laird, married Annie Laurie, daughter of Robert Laurie, the first Baronet of Maxwellton, in 1709. My grandmother is the subject of the widely acclaimed love song in her name composed by William Douglas, one of her previous suitors. My greatest friend is Sir Robert Laurie, my cousin, another of her grandchildren.

Like so many of my lawyer friends, I met Robert Burns for the first time at Lodge Canongate Kilwinning in late 1786. I subscribed to the first Edinburgh Edition. I am also a good friend of Patrick Miller of Dalswinton, his former landlord at Ellisland.

I have met Robert quite often since he moved to Dumfries and, of course, as Provincial Grand Master for that area I know that he was admitted to Lodge St Andrew Kilwinning Dumfries after his move to Ellisland in 1788.

Tragedy had struck my family in the autumn of 1788 when my eldest son, James, died. My wife Deborah was heartbroken and Robert composed the following for her, entitled 'A Mother's Lament':[1]

> Fate gave the word, the arrow sped,
> And pierc'd my Darling's heart;
> And with him all the joys are fled
> Life can to me impart!
>
> By cruel hands the Sapling drops,
> In dust dishonoured laid:

So fell the pride of all my hopes,
My age's future shade.

The mother-linnet in the brake
Bewails her ravish'd young;
So I, for my lost Darling's sake,
Lament the live-day long.

Death, oft I've feared thy fatal blow;
Now, fond, I bare my breast;
O, do thou kindly lay me low
With him I love, at rest!

I am aware that some people scorn Robert for his insularity in outlook, but to me that view is misconceived. For example, early in 1789 Robert composed an elegy on the year 1788 in which it is clear he was knowledgeable about current affairs. He refers to the recent death of Charles III of Spain –'The Spanish Empire's tint a head' – and to political machinations in London. The Prime Minister William Pitt the Younger faced a crisis in that King George III had succumbed to what appeared to be a mental disorder, and the obvious candidate to be appointed Regent was the Prince of Wales. Pitt was aware that the Prince supported Charles James Fox, and would have replaced Pitt as Prime Minister. Robert's pithy take on that was 'The tuilzie's tough 'tween Pitt and Fox'. In the event, the King recovered in February 1789.

Robert journeyed to Edinburgh in February 1789 and successfully resolved two matters which had been greatly troubling him.

About a year previously, while still in Edinburgh, Robert had had what might be described as an emotional entanglement with Mrs Agnes McLehose, a married lady separated from her husband. There is some notoriety associated with the affair, and I know that both her cousin, Lord Craig, and her second cousin, Lord Dreghorn, are very unhappy about it, but Mrs McLehose had assured them that the relationship was platonic. In the event, it transpired that any frustrations Robert suffered by Mrs McLehose keeping him at bay, if indeed she did so (Robert arrived in Edinburgh with a certain reputation), had been assuaged by her maidservant Jenny Clow. She discovered in June 1788 that she was pregnant with Burns's child, and issued a writ *in meditatione fugae* against Robert, the father of her son who was born in October. While in Edinburgh, Burns and his friend Robert Ainslie negotiated a financial settlement with Jenny, and she dropped the proceedings.

Robert had had a great deal of trouble extracting what was due to him from William Creech. I helped Robert obtain a final accounting from Creech and Robert gave him a receipt[2] in the following terms:

Edinburgh, February 27th 1789

Received from Mr Creech Eighteen Pounds Five Shillings Sterling, payment of Fifty-Three copies of my Poems, given to Sir John Whitfoord's Subscribers and calculate twice in the Acct., and also of Twenty more being half of Forty Copies said to be given in presents.

Robert and I agreed the wording of the receipt. Creech had claimed that forty copies had been gifts but could name only twenty recipients, so we demanded he pay the five shillings for the twenty copies he could not account for, as well as for the fifty-three copies previously double counted. By using the phrase 'said to be given in presents', we were leaving it open to claim more from Creech if Robert found out that the alleged donees had not received copies.

Robert thought at the time that Creech had dealt fairly with him, albeit that Creech's dilatoriness had caused him considerable frustration. He estimates that he cleared about £450 from the Edinburgh Edition, but I think that excludes the sale proceeds of the copyright. Robert loaned his brother Gilbert £250 from the proceeds, and, somewhat unwisely, sank the rest into Ellisland.

While the construction of the farmhouse at Ellisland was proceeding – at a snail's pace, according to Robert – he and Jean lodged firstly with David and Agnes Cullie and then with David Newall, a local lawyer, at his property, fairly close to Ellisland. Robert's brother William stayed with them at The Isle, as Newall's property was known, for some time, but at the end of February he left to take up employment as a saddler in Annan, after which he moved to Newcastle and then London, where, sadly, he died the following year. I know that Robert always supported William, both emotionally and financially. William was a fine young man.

A curious sequence of events unfolded in March, prompting Robert to enlist the help of our fellow lawyer, Alexander Cunningham, in Edinburgh in an attempt to avoid damage to his reputation. A short verse entitled 'On the Duchess of Gordon's Reel Dancing'[3] was printed in *The London Star* and attributed to Robert.

> She was the mucklest of them aw;
> Like Saul she stood the tribes aboon;
> Her gown was whiter than the snaw,
> Her face was redder than the moon.

Pure doggerel, obviously, but it was picked up and reproduced by the *London Gazeteer* and *New Daily Advertiser*. The Duchess had been kind to Robert while he was in Edinburgh and had invited Robert to dine at Castle Gordon on one of his tours, so he was concerned partly by the thought of a piece without merit being attributed to him, but more so by the fact that the Duchess might think him ungrateful. Cunningham advised Robert to seek retractions and apologies, both of which were obtained. When printing Robert's disclaimer of authorship and their apology, the publishers of the *Gazeteer* disclosed that the verse had actually been composed by none other than Henry Dundas, then Treasurer of the Navy, following a ball given by the Earl of Findlater. Dundas and the Duchess were intimate friends, and it seemed to me that they had conspired to take Robert down a peg or two by naming him as the author. Robert's reaction was one of anger, as he loathed the Dundas family, and his anger turned to fury when the publishers poked fun at him by qualifying their apology by stating that the verse was not as dull as Robert had insinuated, and they feared that Robert was jealous of Dundas's poetical talents. However, Robert wrote to Cunningham on 4th May thanking him for his concern in what he described as his contest with the London newsmen.

Politics are a dangerous area for Robert, but he cannot resist wading into various controversies, despite my advice that he should be cautious in view of the Excise being such an important element in his financial wellbeing. Even before he received his Excise commission, he was publishing material which, had his identity been known, would have ruled him out of any government service.

It had been imprudent of him to write an open letter to William Pitt published in February 1789 in the *Edinburgh Courant*, with his criticism of government policy towards Scottish distillers, albeit that it bore the nom de plume John Barleycorn, and I told him so. He was also foolish to criticise the monarchy, albeit indirectly, in the satirical poems he had published in the *London Star* on the recovery of the King from what had transpired to be his temporary insanity. These were 'Ode to the Departed Regency Bill' and 'A New Psalm for the Chapel of Kilmarnock'.

In the former[4] he took the opportunity to have a swipe at Henry Dundas:

> Paint Ruin, in the shape of high Dundas
> Gaping with giddy terror o'er the brow

At least he used the noms de plume Agricola and Duncan McLeerie in submitting these parodies for publication.

Back at Ellisland building works were not progressing, and Robert was increasingly frustrated by the delays on the part of the main contractor, Thomas Boyd, and builder, Alexander Crombie. As is well known, Robert's landlord, Patrick Miller, had provided £300 for capital expenditure at Ellisland, to include a farmhouse.

Robert continually had to chase Thomas Boyd to progress the project, using sarcasm, pleading and biblical allusions in his letters. For example, on 8th February 1789 he wrote to Boyd:[5]

> I see at last, dear Sir, some signs of your executing my house within the current year. I am obliidged to set out for Edinburgh se'ennight so I beg you will set as many hands to work as possible during this week. I am distressed with the want of my house in a most provoking manner. It loses me two hours work of my servants every day, besides other inconveniences. For God's sake let me be within the shell of it!
>
> I am, Dear Sir, yours,
>
> Isle, Sunday morn.   Robt. Burns

This direct appeal must have fallen on deaf ears, because on 1st March he had to follow up:[6]

I arrived from Edinburgh yesternight and was a good deal surprised at finding my house still lying like Babylon in the prophesies of Isiah. I beg, dear Sir, for humanity's sake, that you will send me out your hands tomorrow, and oblige.

> Dear Sir, yours,

Isle, Sunday morn.   Robt. Burns

It was only in April 1789 that Robert and Jean were able to move into their new farmhouse.

On occasion Robert's success prompted people he had formerly been acquainted with to approach him for financial assistance. In the summer of 1791, David Sillar, a firm friend from his Lochlie days, was in business difficulties and asked for a loan. Robert put him off:[7]

My dear Sir,

I am extremely sorry to hear of your misfortune, & the more so, as it is not in my power to give you any assistance. I am just five shillings rich at present; tho' I was considerably richer three days ago, when I was obliged to pay twenty pounds for a man who took me in, to save a rotten credit. I heedlessly gave him my name on the back of a bill wherein I had no concern, and he gave me the bill to pay. To write you a long letter, of news &c., would but insult your present unfortunate feelings: I trust your many rich and powerful friends will enable you to get clear of that flinty-hearted scoundrel whos name I detest.

> Yours
> Robt. Burns

What had happened was this: Alexander Crombie, the mason who worked under Boyd at Ellisland, had persuaded Robert to guarantee one of Crombie's debts to the extent of £20, and had been called on to pay the £20 to Crombie's creditor. Robert knew there was little prospect of getting his £20 back from Crombie, but he knew that Boyd owed money to Crombie for work carried out, so he astutely settled his account partly with Crombie's bill.

Although Robert's lease set a commencement date of Martinmas (11th November) 1788, Patrick Miller had allowed him entry to the farm about six months earlier, so it had taken almost eleven months for the farmhouse to be planned, designed and built. Robert and Jean's son Francis-Wallace was born at the new farmhouse that year, around that time Robert's mother brought young Bobbie from Mossgiel to join his family at Ellisland.

When news came from Paris of the storming of the Bastille in July, Robert faced a dilemma. His inclination was to compose a piece in support of the revolutionaries, albeit he was appalled by the summary executions of the Governor and his aides. The aspirations of the French proletariat matched his own hopes for parliamentary reform, but he was conscious that the future wellbeing of his family depended on government service. On this occasion, however, he decided, very wisely, to forego following his heart.

That that proved to be prudent can be seen in Burns's obtaining his appointment as an excise officer in the First Dumfriesshire Itinerary, to commence work in September – good timing for Burns as he had already become disillusioned with farming at Ellisland. His appointment was controversial, because the custom was to appoint officers to a district outwith their area of residence. Not for the first time, Robert's connection with Robert Graham of Fintry had proved invaluable. He also changed the farming operation from arable to dairying, on the basis that, with assistance from servants, Jean could manage the farm while he was on Excise duties.

Before taking up his appointment with the Excise, Robert found time, along with his friend, the lyricist Allan Masterton, to visit his old travelling companion William Nicol, who was on holiday in Moffat. In the course of an extended bout of drinking, they collaborated in composing 'Willie Brewed a Peck o' Maut'[8] in which they are all mentioned in the first verse:

> O Willie brew'd a peck o' maut,
> And Rob and Allan cam to pree;
> Three blyther hearts, that lee-lang night,
> Ye wad na found in Christendie.

Robert had flirted with the landed gentry in Edinburgh, and he continued to try to ingratiate himself in the Dumfriesshire set. Shortly after he took on Ellisland, he was introduced to my cousin, Captain Robert Riddell of Friar's Carse on the Glenriddell Estate, and they became very close. It was an unlikely friendship, as Alexander Young of Harburn, the Edinburgh Writer to the Signet who had been at school with my cousin at Doctor Chapman's in Dumfries, thought my cousin a dull boy and no scholar. To his credit, my cousin was of great assistance to Robert in March 1789 in founding and running the Monkland Friendly Society, a library service for local tenant farmers, to which he contributed many of his own books. That was typical of his Whiggish political and social outlook.

We had some uproarious times at Friar's Carse. I was the winner of the drinking contest which took place there in mid October. The prize was a small ebony whistle which, according to legend, had come into the Riddell family as a result of one of Riddell's ancestors being able to drink a previous owner literally under the table. The rules of the contest at Friar's Carse were simple: whoever was able to blow the whistle after the other contestants could drink no more would keep the whistle as a trophy. My fellow competitors on the night were my cousins Sir Robert Laurie and Glenriddell. John M'Murdo of Drumlanrig was the judge. The third volume of *The Scots Musical Museum*, published in August 1792, includes 'The Whistle', Robert's narrative of the event.[9] He states that he was involved because:

> A bard was selected to witness the fray,
> And tell future ages the feats of the day;

He describes the participants as follows:

> Three joyous good fellows, with hearts clear of flaw;
> Craigdarroch, so famous for wit, worth, and law;
> And trusty Glenriddel, so skilled in old coins;
> And gallant Sir Robert, deep-read in old wines.

After my cousins had succumbed, Robert came into his own:

> Next uprose our Bard, like a prophet in drink: –
> 'Craigdarroch, thou'lt soar when creation shall sink!
> But if thou would flourish immortal in rhyme,
> Come – one bottle more – and have at the sublime!'

I believe I drank more than five bottles of claret to win that whistle!

I think it must have been with considerable hesitation that Robert faced up to the Oath of Abjuration he required to give at the Dumfries Quarter Sessions on 27th October, but, of course, to secure his post with the Excise and thereby his family's financial future, he had no option but to swear:[10]

144

I ROBERT BURNS, residing at Ellisland, by Dumfries, do truly and sincerely acknowledge, profess, testify, and declare in my Conscience before God and the World, that our Sovereign Lord King George is lawful and rightful King of this Realm, and all other his Majesty's Dominions thereunto belonging. And I do solemnly and sincerely declare, That I do believe in my Conscience, that the Person who pretended to be Prince of Wales, during the Life of the late King James, and since his Decease pretending to be and taking upon himself the Stile and Title of King of England, by the Name of James the Third, or of Scotland by the Name of James the Eighth, or the Stile and Title of King of Great Britain, hath not any Right or Title whatsoever to the Crown of this Realm, or any other the Dominions thereto belonging; and I do renounce, refuse and abjure any Allegiance or Obedience to him.

And I do swear. That I will bear faith and true Allegiance to his Majesty King George, and him will defend to the utmost of my Power against all traiterous Conspiracies and Attempts whatsoever, which shall be made against his Person, Crown or Dignity. And I will do my utmost Endeavour to disclose and make known to his Majesty and his Successors, all Treasons and traiterous Conspiracies which I shall know to be against him or any of them.

And I do faithfully promise to the utmost of my Power to support, maintain and defend the Succession of the Crown against him the said James, and all other Persons whatsoever; which Succession (by an Act intituled An Act for the further Limitation of the Crown, and better securing the Rights and Liberties of the Subject) is and stands limited to the Princess

Sophia, late Electress and Dutchess Dowager of Hanover, and the Heirs of her Body, being Protestants. And all these Things I do plainly and sincerely acknowledge and swear, according to these express Words by me spoken, and according to the plain and common Sense and Understanding of the same Words, without any Equivocation, mental Evasion, or secret Reservation whatsoever. And I do make this Recognition, Acknowledgement, Abjuration, Renunciation, and Promise heartily, willingly and truly, upon the true Faith of a Christian.

Robt. Burns

There are many who think that over the last two or three years, Robert has been aware of what might easily be construed as traitorous conspiracies. If he has, he has broken his promise in a spectacular fashion.

Robert did call for me to use my legal talents in assisting his friend Robie Gordon late in 1789. The letter from October 1789[11] to me betrays his jaundiced view of the law. He starts his letter with a misquotation of Psalm 41:

> Blessed be he that kindly doth
> The poor man's case consider.

I have sought you all over the town, good Sir, to learn what you have done, or what can be done, for poor Robie Gordon. The hour is at hand when I must assume the execrable office of whipper-in to the bloodhounds of justice, and must, must let loose the ravenous rage of the carrion sons of bitches on poor Robie. I think you can do something to save the

GROWLING IN THE KENNEL OF JUSTICE

unfortunate man, and am sure, if you can, you will. I
know that benevolence is supreme in your bosom and
has the first voice in, and last check on, all you do; but
that insidious whore, Politics, may seduce the honest
cully Attention, until the practicable moment of doing
is no more.

I have the honor to be, Sir,
your obliged, humble, servant,

Globe Inn, Noon, Wednesday   Robt. Burns

In the event, I was able to keep bloodhounds at bay!

Later

Robert continues to seek my help in legal matters, and I was part of
the array of lawyers who, at his earnest instigation, sought to help
his friend James Clarke in his dispute with the Patrons of Moffat
School.

As a Magistrate in Dumfries in 1792, I was able to exert some
influence resulting in the abandonment of the case against John
Lewars, which was for breach of the peace and assault, as, had it
proceeded, Robert might have had some difficult questions to answer,
and might have found himself in the dock. It helped that David
Newall, Robert's former host at The Isle, was the Fiscal.

I am aware that Robert is very unwell at the present time. Some
scurrilous rumours are circulating that this is due to his drinking. This
is a gross distortion. Take it from someone who knows, so far as
drinking is concerned, Robert cannot compete with the likes of my
cousins and myself. I believe his illness is due to over-exertion when
he was a younger man working long hours at the farms in Ayrshire,

147

possibly inhalation of noxious substances when he was engaged in the flax-dressing business, and his duties as an excise officer in the First Dumfriesshire Itinerary.

CHAPTER 12

THE END OF THE IDYLL

1790

WILLIAM DUNBAR WS

William Dunbar was admitted a Writer to the Signet in Edinburgh on 4th July 1769. He was Depute-Master of the Lodge Canongate Kilwinning. A supporter of wider electoral franchise, he was a member of the Standing Committee of the Convention for Reform. He was also a leading light in the gentleman's club known as 'The Crochallan Fencibles'. He was a subscriber to the first Edinburgh Edition.

Dunbar had a close friendship with Burns during his Edinburgh period, and after Burns's move to Dumfriesshire, they continued to correspond. Dunbar was invited to comment on drafts of new poems and songs from time to time. Burns described him as a judicious, candid friend.

Dunbar was appointed Inspector-General of Stamp Duties for Scotland. He died, unmarried, in 1807.

My name is William Dunbar. I am a Writer to the Signet. I make this statement on 31st May 1806.

I first met Robert Burns when he came to Edinburgh in 1786. I was introduced to him by Harry Erskine, then Dean of the Faculty of Advocates. We were all Freemasons, our lodge being Canongate Kilwinning. At the time I was Depute Master of the Lodge, and a Colonel in the club known as the 'Crochallan Fencibles'. Henry Mackenzie has described what we got up to at the club.

I took to Robert immediately, had no hesitation in inviting him to join the Fencibles, and he passed our initiation test with enthusiasm. He certainly kept us entertained at the club with his bawdy poems, many of which he included in his collection known as *The Merry Muses of Caledonia*, published posthumously for the Fencibles in 1800.

Robert was a very close friend of mine while he was in Edinburgh. He paid me a real compliment at the time by referring to me in his version of the traditional Borders song 'Rattlin' Roarin' Willie'[1] included in the second volume of *The Scots Musical Museum* published in 1788, the final verse of which reads:

> As I cam by Crochallan,
> I cannilie keekit ben,
> Rattlin, roaring Willie
> Was sitting at yon boord-en',
> Sitting at yon boord-en',
> And amang guid companie;
> Rattlin, roarin Willie,
> Ye're welcome hame to me.

In April 1787, when he was contemplating moving out of Edinburgh back to the country, Robert wrote a touching letter[2] to me, including the following passage:

Dear Sir

… The time is approaching when I shall return to my
shades; and I am afraid my numerous Edinburgh
friendships are of so tender a construction, that they
will not bear carriage with me. Yours is one of the few
that I could wish of a more robust constitution. It is
indeed very probable that when I leave this city, we
part never more to meet in this sublunary sphere; but
I have a strong fancy that in some future eccentric
planet, the comet of happier systems than any with
which astronomy is yet acquainted, you and I, among
the harum scarum sons of imagination and whim,
with a hearty shake of a hand, a metaphor and a laugh,
shall recognise old acquaintances… .

> I have the honor to be,
> with the warmest sincerity,
> Dr. Sir, your oblidged & very
> humble servant,

Lawnmarket   Robert Burns

After moving to Ellisland, Robert continued to correspond with
many of his former friends in the Fencibles, so I was aware that he
had joined the Excise. I received a letter from him in January 1790. In
this he mentioned to me that the £50 salary from the Excise was a
useful – almost essential – supplement to his income from the farm,
from which I inferred that the farming business was not going well.
Indeed, it was difficult to work out how it could be a success, since he
was riding on his Excise matters at least two hundred miles every week.
But he assured me he had not by any means given up the Muses. His
brother Gilbert later told me that by the beginning of the year, Robert
was saying that Ellisland had undone his enjoyment of himself.

Although Robert knew I was unmarried and without children, he chose to share with me his thoughts on fatherhood. Here is an excerpt from his letter of 14th January 1790:[3]

Dear Sir,

... But, my dear Sir, little ones that look up to you for paternal protection are an important charge. I have already two fine, healthy, stout little fellows, and I wish to throw some light upon them. I have a thousand reveries and schemes about them and their future destiny. Not that I am an Utopian projector in these things. I am resolved never to breed up a son of mine to any of the learned professions. I know the value of independence; and since I cannot give my sons an independent fortune, I shall give them an independent line of life. What a chaos of hurry, chance, and changes is this world, when one sits soberly down to reflect on it! To a father, who himself knows the world, the thought that he shall have sons to usher into it must fill him with dread; but if he have daughters, the prospect in a thoughtful moment is apt to shock him...

Yours sincerely,
Ellisland, January 1790   Robert Burns

I must say I found this to be the most extraordinary paragraph, if for no reason other than its complete illogicality. It is one of the outstanding features of being in a profession such as the Law or Medicine that one achieves and retains independence. I have never understood what Robert was driving at, particularly as he had told me a couple of years previously that he was breeding his son Bobbie up for the Church. In fairness, perhaps the Church is more of a calling than a profession.

The third volume of Johnson's *The Scots Musical Museum* appeared in February. Robert's contribution included a tongue-in-cheek commentary on the implications of the French Revolution on the Whig party, which was prescient:[4]

CHORUS
Awa Whigs awa,
Awa Whigs awa,
Ye're but a pack o'traitor louns,
Ye'll do nae guid at a'

VERSES
Our thrissles flourish'd fresh and fair,
And bonie bloom'd our roses;
But Whigs cam like a frost in June,
And wither'd a' our posies.

Our ancient crown's fa'n in the dust;
Deil blin' them wi' the stoure o't,
And write their names in his black beuk
Wha gae the Whigs the power o't!

Our sad decay in church and state
Surpasses my descriving:
The Whigs cam o'er us for a curse,
And we have done wi'thriving.

Grim Vengeance lang has ta'en a nap,
But we may see him wauken;
Gude help the day when Royal heads
Are hunted like a maukin!

Whigs were widely distrusted by the Government following their support of the aspirations of the American colonists and at the time were perceived to be secretly in sympathy with the French. The Whig movement for reform of the electoral system in Scotland, of which I was a part, in effect ground to a halt. It would be more than a decade before we could safely hold meetings to promote reform.

Robert had taken a great interest in the legal case surrounding a lady he described as his "poor namesake", one Margaret Burns. She was young, beautiful and occupied a property in Rose Street in Edinburgh. In August the previous year she had been accused of breach of the public peace.

I suspect that Robert's interest was kindled by a familiarity with the Margarets of this world, and also by the fact that she was represented by his friend, the advocate Alexander Abercromby, who was part of the literary circle in Edinburgh. Abercromby was also an associate of Henry Mackenzie, and had contributed to Mackenzie's periodicals *The Mirror* and *The Lounger*. Abercromby was, of course, a subscriber to the first Edinburgh Edition. Robert also knew that his publisher, William Creech, was involved in the case.

The charge against Margaret was that she and her friend Sally Sanderson, being persons of bad character, kept a brothel or common bawdy house in Rose Street, into which they admitted and entertained licentious and profligate persons of both sexes, to the great annoyance of the neighbourhood. There were allegations of fighting, cursing and swearing on the property and the entry thereto, and of singing and other improper behaviour on Sundays.

The Fiscal had asked the Bailies of the city to impose a fine or other punishment as they might think fit, and to ordain that the accused be removed from the house. Margaret had not been present when the evidence was taken, but in her absence, the Bailies had ordered that she be banished forth of the city and liberties forever, and that if she be found in the city, be imprisoned for six months, drummed through the city and again banished forever.

Creech was one of the Bailies who imposed this extraordinary sentence, which was intimated to Margaret on 1st October 1789, though he had the sense to defer compliance until 5th October. That enabled Margaret to engage Abercromby to lodge an appeal to the Court of Session by way of a Bill of Suspension, and the judge, another of Robert's subscribers, Lord Dreghorn, ordered the fiscal to lodge Answers to the Bill. When the matter came before Lord Ankerville, he refused it and Abercromby appealed to the Inner House.[5]

By this time the unfairness of the procedure and the disproportionate nature of the sentence had become apparent, and the fiscal did not oppose the appeal in the Inner House. Lord President Ilay Campbell passed the Bill of Consent. In effect, the conviction was quashed.

In an excerpt from his letter dated 2nd February 1790[6] to his Edinburgh bookseller, Peter Hill, Robert made clear where his sympathies lay:

Dear Sir

… how is the fate of my poor namesake Mademoiselle Burns decided? Which of their grave LORDSHIPS can lay his hand on his heart and say that he has not taken advantage of such frailty? Nay, if we may judge by near six thousand years' experience, can the world do without such frailty? …

My dear Sir, ever Yours,
Ellisland, 2nd Feb., 1790   Robt. Burns

Robert also wrote an epigram, 'Under the Portrait of Miss Burns':[7]

> Cease, ye prudes, your envious railings,
> Lovely Burns has charms: confess!
> True it is that she had one failing:
> Had a woman ever less?

Robert continued with his study of literature and subscribed to many periodicals, including Henry Mackenzie's *Lounger*. On 10th April, he wrote from Ellisland to his patron Mrs Frances Dunlop about an article he had just read:[8]

Dear Madam,

I have just now, my ever honoured friend, enjoyed a very high luxury, in reading a paper of the Lounger. You know my national prejudices. I had often read and admired the Spectator, Adventurer, Rambler, and World; but still with a certain regret, that they were so thoroughly and entirely English. Alas! have I often said to myself, what are all the boasted advantages which my country reaps from the Union, that can counterbalance the annihilation of her independence, and even her very name!

I have the honor to be, Madam,
Your obliged humble servant.

Ellisland   Robt. Burns

This was a dangerous sentiment for a government employee to express. It is a measure of the confidence Robert had in Mrs Dunlop's discretion.

Lord Monboddo had welcomed Robert into his home while he was in Edinburgh, and Robert had composed lines in praise of Monboddo's daughter Eliza. Sadly, Eliza suffered from respiratory problems, and in 1790 her condition deteriorated. Monboddo sent her to the Braid Hills, south of the city, in the hope that the clearer air there would help. But it was to no avail, and on 17th June 1790, she passed away. Burns composed an epitaph for her, the first and last verses of which are set out here:[9]

> Life ne'er exulted in so rich a prize
> As Burnet, lovely from her native skies;
> Nor envious Death so triumph'd in a blow
> As that which laid th' accomplish'd Burnet low.
>
> The Parent's heart that nestled fond in thee,
> That heart how sunk, a prey to grief and care!
> So deck'd the woodbine sweet yon aged tree;
> So, rudely ravish'd, left it bleak and bare!

In July there was an election in the Dumfries Burghs. The sitting member was Sir James Johnston, a Tory, and he was being opposed by the Whig, Patrick Miller Junior, the son of Robert's landlord at Ellisland. The election was more about the personalities than party politics, in that Miller was supported by both the Duke of Queensberry and Henry Dundas, neither of whom could be described as being a reformer. Miller was undoubtedly the Establishment candidate. Robert was directed by his landlord to escort young Miller to the election hustings. It was anticipated that there would be an acrimonious and possibly violent confrontation between both sets of supporters, but Robert was unconcerned, trusting, as he put it, to "the heels of my horse, which are among the best in Nithsdale".[10]

In the event, the meeting fizzled out without any trouble. The election was won by Miller, his campaign having been masterminded by the lawyer John Bushby. Robert had supported Johnston, because of his mistrust of Queensberry's Whig credentials and his hatred of Dundas. He wrote two ballads about the election, and in this verse from the 'Election Ballad for Westerha'', which he sent to Robert Graham of Fintry, one can discern the fact that he was aware at that time that he had better keep his political views to himself:[11]

> For your poor friend, the Bard, afar
> He only hears and sees the war,
> A cool Spectator purely!
> So, when the storm the forest rends,
> The Robin in the hedge descends,
> And sober chirps securely.

I kept Robert up to date with developments in the legal case which had so engaged his attention while he was in Edinburgh. The case, *Maxwell-Campbell* v. *Montgomery*, in which Robert's friend Montgomery was being sued for damages for seducing Maxwell-Campbell's wife, had, by this time, been dragging on for four years. It was a tragedy worthy of a novel in itself. After the rejection of the preliminary objection by Montgomery, evidence was taken from a wide number of witnesses. While that was going on, David Guthrie, the tenant farmer who had loaned Maxwell-Campbell £120 14s. about four years previously, lodged an arrestment in the hands of each of Montgomery and his agent, the effect of which was to ensure that his debt would be paid first out of anything that was found to be due to Maxwell-Campbell. Then, in 1789, Mrs Maxwell-Campbell tragically died and her husband commenced proceedings to bastardise the boy alleged to be Montgomery's son. In the original damages case, on 26th June 1790, the Court of Session awarded Maxwell-Campbell

£200 to be paid at £20 per annum over ten years, but Montgomery appealed and the award was reduced to £120 plus expenses of £334. By this time, numerous others of Maxwell-Campbell's creditors had lodged arrestments, so Montgomery raised an action of Multiplepoinding in the same way as Robert's father had done in respect of his tenancy dispute. I doubt if Maxwell-Campbell recovered any damages himself.

The work and long hours of travel involved in the First Dumfries Itinerary were proving to be arduous for Robert, and he decided once again to see if he could engineer a promotion by way of favours from friends. He wrote to Mrs Dunlop in March that a transfer to a port division would be both lucrative and less taxing, and dropped a none-too-subtle hint that William Corbet, husband of her friend, one of the two General Supervisors of Excise in Scotland, could pave the way for him, while cautioning that any overt canvassing on his behalf would be prejudicial to his hopes. Mrs Dunlop seems to have been up to the task, for in July, Robert obtained a transfer to the Dumfries Third Division, a foot walk. This meant that, for the moment, Robert was travelling from Ellisland to Dumfries and back on a daily basis, though on occasion he stayed overnight at the Globe tavern, which was to have familiar and predictable consequences nine months later.

Robert himself suffered loss at this time. In September, he received a letter from his former schoolteacher John Murdoch who was at the time residing in London. Robert's younger brother William had taken employment as a journeyman saddler in The Strand. Robert often expressed his concern at William's lack of ambition and his difficulties in living within his income, and in July, Robert had asked Murdoch to look in on the lad (who was only twenty-three) to give him some advice. Murdoch received the letter on 26th July, and at the same time had news that William was ill. He called to see him on the morning of the 27th but found that William had passed away on the

24th. Why Murdoch delayed writing to Robert for two months was never explained.

It was difficult to discern Robert's attitude to lawyers at this time. For example, he had been approached for advice by John Wilson in relation to a post as legal clerk. Wilson had been the schoolmaster at Tarbolton, but had found that, in order to make ends meet, he needed a second income, and had opened a shop in the village from which he sold, among other things, health cures. Robert had endured listening to Wilson airing his scanty medical knowledge at a meeting of the local Masonic Lodge, and some years later had composed his satire on Wilson entitled 'Death and Doctor Hornbook'. Wilson then became keen to start a third new life as a legal clerk in Edinburgh. Robert tried to dissuade Wilson, advising that the life of an Edinburgh quill-driver at twopence a page was a life he knew so well that he should be very sorry if any friend of his should ever try it. If Wilson went ahead, he would be sure to have before him a life of many sorrows. He did, however, give Wilson a letter of introduction to my colleague John Somerville, another subscriber to the Edinburgh Edition.

By way of contrast, Burns recommended the employment of William Duncan to his friend Crauford Tait, my fellow Writer to the Signet in Edinburgh. Duncan was the son of an old friend from Ayrshire. It is interesting that in this letter Robert admits to being the worst hand in the world at asking a favour. Perhaps that was true, but he certainly had a lot of practice in doing so! Having been newly appointed to a foot walk in Dumfries using Mrs Dunlop's connections, he was now seeking further advancement in the Excise, and craved Robert Graham of Fintry to engineer his promotion to Supervisor in Port Glasgow, Greenock or Dumfries. Robert must have known that Graham would by now be thoroughly tired of his behaviour, because he preceded his latest request for preferment by admitting he did not like to be "an incessant beggar from you". Graham was unable to do anything for Robert that time.

Bob Ainslie, my fellow Writer to the Signet and Freemason, visited Robert at Ellisland in the autumn. Bob had been informed by William Nicol that Robert was about to be promoted in the Excise, and Nicol was concerned that Robert's elevated station would cause him to lose touch with his old friends. Bob and Nicol had determined to bring Robert down to earth if that happened, but this turned out to be a *brutum fulmen* – Nicol had been misinformed, and Robert never achieved high office in the Excise.

When Bob arrived at Ellisland, he found Robert in good spirits, though he had been unwell during the harvest and said he had been low in spirits following the death of his brother. Having received his promotion to the foot walk in Dumfries, he was delighted that he was no longer obliged to undertake exhausting rides all over the county, inspecting dirty ponds and yeasty barrels, which had played havoc with his health.

Bob was told that Robert had the reputation of adopting a sympathetic attitude in court proceedings against defaulters who were impoverished, which seemed to have brought him credit with the justices, in that they imposed substantial fines on those Robert regarded as being well able to pay. This had resulted in Robert's commission, for assisting in convictions, being double the norm for an exciseman.

One of his Excise cases had caused him difficulty, however. Thomas Johnston, a local farmer, had been fined £5 for making malt illegally, and had appealed to the justices. On his return to Edinburgh, Bob showed me the Answers Robert had prepared to the Petition presented to the justices by Johnston. Although Robert wrongly pleaded evidence as part of his Answers, they showed he had a pretty good grasp of the law:[12]

1. Whether the Petitioner has been in use formerly to malt all his grain at one operation, is foreign to the purpose; this last season he certainly malted his crop at four or five operations; but be that as it may, Mr J. ought to have known that by express Act of Parliament no malt, however small the quantity, can be legally manufactured until previous entry be made in writing of all the ponds, barns, floors, &c., so as to be used before the grain can be put to steep. In the Excise entry-books for the division, there is not a syllable of T. J.'s name for a number of years bygone.

2. True it is that Mr Burns, on his first ride, in answer to Mr J.'s question anent the conveying of the notices, among other ways pointed out the sending it by post as the most eligible method, but at the same time added this express clause, and to which Mr Burns is willing to make faith: "At the same time, remember, Mr J., that the notice is at your risk until it reach me!" Further, when Mr Burns came to the Petitioner's kiln, there was a servant belonging to Mr J. ploughing at a very considerable distance from the kiln, who left his plough and three horses without a driver, and came into the kiln, which Mr Burns thought was rather a suspicious circumstance, as there was nothing so extraordinary in an Excise-officer going into a legal malt-floor so as to induce a man to leave three horses yoked to a plough in the distant middle of a moor. This servant, on being repeatedly questioned by Mr Burns, could not tell when the malt was put to steep, when it was taken out, &c.–in short, was determined to be entirely ignorant of the affair. By and by, Mr J.'s son came in; and on being questioned as to the steeping, taking out of the grain, &c., Mr J., junior, referred me to this said servant, this

ploughman, who, he said, must remember it best, as having been the principal actor in the business. The lad then, having gotten his cue, circumstantially recollected all about it.

3. All this time, though I was telling the son and servant the nature of the premunire they had incurred, though they pleaded for mercy keenly, the affair of the notice having been sent never once occurred to them, not even the son, who is said to have been the bearer. This was a stroke reserved for, and worthy of, the gentleman himself. As to Mrs Kelloch's oath, it proves nothing. She did, indeed, depone to a line being left for me at her house, which said line miscarried. It was a sealed letter: she could not tell whether it was a malt-notice or not; she could not even condescend on the month, nor so much as the season of the year. The truth is T. J. and his family being Seceders, and consequently coming every Sunday to Thornhill Meeting-house, they were a good conveyance for the several maltsters and traders in their neighbourhood to transmit to post their notices, permits, &c.

4. But why all this tergiversation? It was put to the Petitioner in open court, after a full investigation of the cause: "Was he willing to swear that he meant no fraud in the matter?" And the justices told him, that if he swore, he would be assoilzied, otherwise he should be fined; still the Petitioner, after ten minutes' consideration, found his conscience unequal to the task, and declined the oath.

5. Now, indeed, he says he is willing to swear: he has been exercising his conscience in private, and will perhaps stretch a point. But the fact to which he is to swear was equally and

in all parts known to him on that day when he refused to swear as to-day: nothing can give him further light as to the intention of his mind, respecting his meaning or not meaning a fraud in the affair. No time can cast further light on the present resolves of the mind; but time will reconcile, and has reconciled, many a man to that iniquity which he at first abhorred.

Bob told me that the impression I had gained at the beginning of the year was correct, and Robert's experiences over the previous year had driven him to the conclusion that farming did not suit him, and he was determined to give it up for good. As ever with Robert, however, there was a complication. Robert had confided in Bob that he was about to be delivered of two more children, but this time by different mothers. His wife was expecting a child in the New Year, and so was Anna Park, the barmaid at the Globe tavern, Robert's favourite hostelry in Dumfries. When Bob asked Robert about the implications of this, he airily dismissed it, saying that Anna's child would in all probability be treated in the same way as his daughter Bess: kept in the family with all the other children. And some months after the child was born, she did in fact join the Burns ménage in Dumfries.

Bob asked Robert about his poetry, and he said he was completing the composition of an epic poem about a drunken farmer who interrupts a witches' dance at Alloway Kirk. He quoted a couple of verses, and Bob thought it rather exciting. Of course, it later emerged as his famous 'Tam o' Shanter', published the following April.

Later

I was quite concerned for Robert's wellbeing when Bob recounted how he had found him at Ellisland, and I wrote a number of letters to him, but I received no reply until January 1791, when he assured me he was not gone to Elysium, but was still in the sublunary world, serving his God. And as a further proof that he was still in the land of existence, he sent me 'Tam o' Shanter'. I regard it as Robert's finest work.

CHAPTER 13

THE TRANSITION

1791

JOHN SYME

John Syme's father was a Writer to the Signet and the Laird of Barncailzie in Kirkcudbrightshire.

Syme was a military man and after retirement from the Army, he became an estate factor. As such he had opportunities to acquire considerable knowledge of legal forms, particularly as regards factory accounts, though he never studied the Law as a profession. He became Collector of Stamps for Dumfries, and moved there in 1791. Syme accompanied Burns on tours of Galloway in 1793 and 1794, and enlisted in the Royal Dumfries Volunteers with him in 1795.

Syme was a Freemason and one of the main members of the Committee of Trustees which collected and administered funds for the benefit of Burns's family after his death.

John Syme died in 1831.

My name is John Syme. I am sixty-five years of age. I make this statement on 31st March 1820.

My father was a lawyer and owned a large country estate in Kirkcudbrightshire. He hoped I would follow him in the Law but I gravitated towards the Army, and after my service, I hoped to enjoy the life of a country gentleman at our estate at Barncailzie. Unfortunately, my father was a partner in the Douglas Heron Bank, and as a result of his unlimited liability for the Bank's debts, Barncailzie had to be sold. I had to obtain employment and I became an estate factor and the Collector of Stamps for Dumfries. My office was on the ground floor of a house in the Wee Vennel.

Robert and I got on well, and he was a frequent guest at Ryedale, my house in Dumfries. As mentioned, although I was not in practice as a lawyer, I had many friends who were lawyers and was very familiar with the Edinburgh legal establishment. Robert kept me entertained with his stories of his many brushes with the law, both in Ayrshire and in Edinburgh. I had in fact been introduced to Robert in Edinburgh in 1787 by my lawyer friend, Alexander Cunningham.

We often discussed the political developments in France. Contrary to the perception now, the Revolution there was welcomed in Great Britain by Whigs and Tories alike. The Whigs were pleased that the French had been freed from absolute despotism, and the Tories liked the idea that the French would be preoccupied with internal affairs rather than challenging British interests around the world, although they did have a concern that French ideas about reform might spread to Great Britain.

Robert himself had been sure that the French Revolution would inspire parliamentary reform in Scotland, which was much needed. The franchise in Scotland was even more limited than in the rest of Great Britain, extending to less than 1 per cent of the population, with both the lower and middle classes almost entirely excluded. Many landowners too were disenfranchised, as votes rested with their feudal superiors. In the towns and cities, corruption was rife, with widespread cliques and cronyism.

For over ten years prior to 1791, power in Scotland had rested in practice with the lawyer Henry Dundas. He was a son of the late Lord President, Robert Dundas the Younger, and the half-brother of the Lord Chief Baron Robert Dundas, so he had as many advantages in progressing a legal career as one could wish for. He had been appointed Solicitor General in 1766, then Lord Advocate in 1775. He had built up a kind of informal government in Scotland, controlling thirty-four of the forty-one Scottish constituencies in the previous decade. He acted as a satrap. Robert disliked him and everything he stood for with great intensity.

In the mid 1780s some of Robert's Whig friends in Edinburgh had formed a committee seeking to extend the franchise while keeping it within the property-owning classes. The standing committee of this Convention for Reform included Harry Erskine, then Dean of Faculty; the advocates Robert Cullen, Archibald Fletcher, John Clerk and Adam Gillies; the judge Lord Gardenstone; William Dunbar, Robert's lawyer friend from the Crochallan Fencibles; and Robert Graham of Fintry, his patron in the Excise. For seven years they had been pressing for reform, but had been frustrated at every turn by Dundas. In May 1791 there was a debate in the House of Commons, when reform was moved by Richard Sheridan and seconded by Charles Fox. As usual, it was opposed by Dundas, but his opposition was formal only and a second motion was moved by Fox and Harry Erskine's brother Thomas, as a result of which it was agreed that the question of reform would be considered by the House early in the next session of Parliament. It seemed to Robert that his liberal friends were at last making progress towards reform of the franchise.

As mentioned, they were attempting to break the stranglehold the feudal superiors had on government in Scotland. Robert, of course, would have preferred to go further. In this aim he had been inspired by the publication of *Rights of Man* by Thomas Paine in February 1791. Robert was now keener than ever to support the movement for reform, despite being in government service.

Other issues were preying on his mind, however. In the early part of the year he was extremely affected by the death (in January) of Lord Glencairn, who had been a tremendous support to him when he first arrived in Edinburgh, and who he described as his best friend, and his first and dearest patron and benefactor. Personally, I think that honour rests with the Ayr lawyer Robert Aiken, but in any event, the aftermath of Glencairn's death at the age of forty-two upset Robert more than the death itself. Robert was anxious to attend the memorial service, but he was not invited. He also composed a lament for Glencairn, and wrote to each of the deceased's sisters, Lady Betty Cunningham and Lady Harriet Don, with a copy. Neither even acknowledged his letter.

Robert's latest children were born within ten days of one another. Surprisingly, his illegitimate daughter, Elizabeth Park, born on 31st March, was later given up by her mother Anna to Robert's family, and she was cared for and brought up by Jean Burns in Dumfries.

I mentioned earlier my friend Alexander Cunningham. Robert enlisted his help in June on behalf of his friend James Clarke, the schoolmaster in Moffat, who was threatened with dismissal as a result of complaints made about his over-zealous use of corporal punishment towards his pupils. This excerpt from Burns's letter to Cunningham of 11th June[1] betrayed a less than optimistic view of the educational prospects for some of the children under the watch of masters like Clarke:

God help the teacher, a man of sensibility and genius, and such is my friend Clarke, when the booby father presents him his booby son, and insists on lighting up the rays of science in a fellow's head whose skull is impervious and inaccessible by any other way than a positive fracture with a cudgel!

The case against Clarke would be determined by the administrators of the school, who were the ministers and magistrates of Edinburgh Town Council, and Cunningham agreed to represent Clarke. Robert himself drafted some preliminary representations to the Council for signature by Clarke. I could not have improved on them.

An interesting exchange of correspondence ensued in July between Robert and his former inamorata Mrs Agnes McLehose. Robert wrote to her[2] expressing his concern about what he could, in safety, include in his letters to her:

How can you expect a Correspondent should write you when you declare that you mean to preserve his letters with a view, sooner or later, to expose them to the pillory of derision and the rack of criticism? This is gagging me completely as to speaking the sentiments of my bosom;

Her reply of 2nd August[3] was categoric, and later events confirmed her determination to keep the letters secret:

You surely mistake me, Sir.–"Expose your letters to criticism!" Nothing could be further from my intention: read my letters and you will find nothing to justify such an idea. But I suppose they are burned, so you can't have recourse to them. In an impassioned hour I once talked of publishing them, but a little cool reflection showed me its impropriety: the idea has been long abandoned and I wish you to write me with that confidence you would do to a person of whom you entertained a good opinion and who is sincerely interested in your welfare. To the 'every day children of the world' I well know one cannot speak the sentiments of the bosom.

By the middle of the year, Robert was running down his activities on the farm at Ellisland, having exhausted what little capital remained from the first Edinburgh Edition. He and his landlord, Patrick Miller, reached an agreement in principle that the tack or lease could be given up with effect from 11th November 1791. Patrick had been approached by his neighbour John Morine about the possibility of his purchasing Ellisland with vacant possession. I imagine Morine must have been aware that Robert's heart was no longer in farming Ellisland, and he was astute in using that knowledge to his advantage. Robert readily agreed to quit, as he had insufficient capital to continue farming. He sold his crops by auction in late August, and after the roup was over, taking full advantage of Robert's hospitality, a drunken melee involving about thirty neighbours and friends ensued. Robert described it as such a scene of drunkenness as was hardly ever seen in the country.

I advised Robert on the wording of the simple renunciation of the lease that he completed on 10th September. Under this, he narrated that he had paid the rents of the farm of Ellisland to the term of Martinmas 1791, and settled his accounts relating thereto with his landlord and accordingly forever renounced his lease.

Robert and his expanded family moved to the small flat above my office in November. His vacating of Ellisland was not without incident. His relationship with his landlord cooled for a while, and at one point he compared Patrick's treatment of him with that of his Edinburgh publisher William Creech, which had been a very unhappy episode in his life. This was extremely unfair, as I know that Patrick was generous towards Robert in the final settlement between them. But Robert also contrived to fall out with John Morine, the incoming proprietor.

In December I was with Robert for dinner at Tinwald Downs, the country house of my friend John Bushby, a local lawyer and man of business, who also acted as the election agent for Henry Dundas in our area. Robert asked us whether he should do anything further in respect of what he described as a trifling matter arising out of the handover of Ellisland to Morine. Robert was being required to pay for dilapidations. It transpired that Morine and Robert had not seen eye to eye on these, and in a fit of pique, Robert had exacerbated the situation by arranging for his brother-in-law, Adam Armour, to smash all the windows at the farmhouse, which had been engraved by Robert, for fear that Morine would gain a financial advantage by becoming owner of them. We advised Robert to accept whatever the arbiters decided. In the event, as can be seen from the finding,[4] Robert's foolishness cost him at least six shillings in additional costs:

Elisland, 19th. Jan., 1792

We, Joseph Hanning, in Merkland, and Patrick Barr, in McCubbinstown, Barley-Men, at the desire of Mr John Morrin of Laggan, we went this day and viewed the Houses upon Elisland lately possessed by Mr Robert Burns, and finds that the Byre and Stable will take ten shillings for thatch and workmanship, the Barn thirteen shillings for thatch and workmanship, the Dwelling House for Glass Six

Shillings, for sclate and workmanship five shillings. This we give as our opinion to put the House in a tenantable condition.

Patrick Barr
Joseph Hanning

Never one to miss an opportunity to lampoon, Robert got revenge of sorts in his 'Epigram on the Laird of Laggan'[5] about Morine:

> When Morine, deceas'd to the Devil went down,
> 'Twas nothing would serve him, but Satan's own crown;
> 'Thy fool's head', quoth Satan, 'that crown shall wear never:
> I grant thou'rt as wicked, but not quite so clever.'

I know that towards the end of the year Robert was concerned about the welfare of Jenny Clow, the former servant of Mrs McLehose. The girl had borne Robert's child – called Robert Clow Burns – in 1788. She was now in straitened circumstances. In November Robert received an appeal from Mrs McLehose to do something to support the girl, and he immediately wrote requesting that she send a porter to Jenny with five shillings in his name, and tell her that he would be in Edinburgh the following week and try what was to be done for her relief. I believe while there Robert settled some monies on the girl, but though she was at death's door with a consumptive illness, Robert could not prevail upon her to allow him to take their three-year-old son back to Dumfries. In fact, Robert Clow Burns survived, since when he has married and his own son, also called Robert, was born this year (1820).

While in Edinburgh Robert met with Mrs McLehose for what proved to be the final time. After they parted, Robert sent her three songs said to have been inspired by her, including the wonderful 'Ae Fond Kiss'.

The accommodation at Robert's flat above my office was anything but commodious, but both Mrs Burns and he seemed relieved that the burden of running the farm had been lifted from them. According to Mrs Burns, the sale in August was a very good one, well attended, and had raised a considerable sum for their comfort in the new situation.

Robert's fortunes in 1791 were mixed. On the one hand, 'Tam o' Shanter' had been acclaimed, and his work on the fourth volume of *The Scots Musical Museum* was going well. He had a wide circle of like-minded friends in and around Dumfries. On the other hand he had suffered injury – a broken arm when he fell with his horse – and illness, and he had finally broken with Mrs McLehose. But, on balance, at the end of the year there was optimism that his new situation in town marked a fresh start for the family. The only cloud on the horizon that I could see was his inability to keep his political views out of the public domain.

Later

Robert was one of my closest friends. In 1792 he accompanied me when I was admitted an affiliate brother Freemason at the Lodge St Andrew Dumfries. We toured the south-west in his later years.

I was sad that Robert took to denigrating my friend John Bushby for his political views, and his son Maitland, an advocate, for what Robert saw as his 'dim wittedness'.

After Robert's death I was closely involved in the financial arrangements made for his widow and children. I was offered the opportunity to be Robert's biographer, but declined the role. I have since learned that Maria Riddell, one of Robert's closest friends in

Dumfries, was less than enthusiastic about my being the biographer, and, somewhat unkindly, described me as a careless character, totally disorganised in business matters, and lost in a mist of my own creation. Thankfully my great friend James Currie took on the task.

It has emerged that the late Robert Graham of Fintry may have been masquerading as a supporter of the Convention for Reform, as he later provided intelligence about the reform movement to Henry Dundas.

CHAPTER 14

SIREN SONGS

1792

ALEXANDER FRASER TYTLER, LORD WOODHOUSELEE

Alexander Fraser Tytler, Lord Woodhouselee, was an advocate, writer and historian.

He was educated at the High School in Edinburgh and the University of Edinburgh. Admitted to the Faculty of Advocates in 1770, he was appointed Professor of Universal History and Greek and Roman Antiquities in the University of Edinburgh in 1776, a post he held until 1800.

Tytler became a Court of Session judge in 1801, adopting the title Lord Woodhouselee, the name of his family's country estate near Penicuik.

He died in 1813.

My name is Fraser Tytler. I have the judicial title Lord Woodhouselee. I am sixty-five years of age. I make this statement on 31st October 1812.

I was a subscriber to Burns's first Edinburgh Edition and a great admirer of his works. In 1791 I was in correspondence with him following the publication of his narrative poem 'Tam O' Shanter' in the *Edinburgh Magazine*. I considered it a classic, and advised Burns that unless I was much mistaken, that poem alone, had he never written another syllable, would have been sufficient to have transmitted his name to posterity. However, I was uncomfortable with the following lines:[1]

> Three lawyers' tongues, turn'd inside out,
> Wi' lies seam'd like a beggar's clout;
> Three priests' hearts, rotten, black as muck,
> Lay stinking, vile in every neuk.

Burns replied to me in what he described as grateful acknowledgement. As to my suggestion regarding the above lines, he agreed to cut out what he described as "the hit at the lawyer and priest",[2] and they were removed from the second Edinburgh Edition in 1793.

At the end of January 1792, I had occasion to dine at the Edinburgh townhouse of Alexander Fergusson of Craigdarroch in St Andrew Square. There I met his cousin Walter Riddell, brother of Robert Riddell of Glenriddell, and Walter's young wife Maria. They had recently moved from London to Goldielea in Dumfriesshire following the birth of their first child in August 1791, and while Goldielea was being renovated for them – it was later renamed Woodley Park, Woodley being Maria's maiden name – they stayed with Robert Riddell at Friar's Carse. There Maria had met Burns, who of course was Robert Riddell's greatest friend at the time, and Burns had encouraged Maria to find a publisher for her book *Voyages to the Madeira and Leeward Caribbean isles: with sketches of the natural history of these islands.* One purpose of her visit to Edinburgh was to meet William Smellie, the printer of Burns's first Edinburgh Edition, to whom Burns had written a letter of introduction on her behalf. In the event, the book was later published by Peter Hill in Edinburgh and Thomas Cadell in London. This paragraph in the introduction,[3] somewhat self-effacing, may well be directed at Burns as one of the friends 'partial' to the authoress:

> Such, however, as it is, I will submit it to your inspection, and that of a few friends, whose partiality, perhaps, for the writer, more than any intrinsic merit it can lay claim to, may incline them to regard it in a favourable point of view.

At dinner I was a little taken aback by the frankness with which the nineteen-year-old Maria spoke, and her effusive praise of Burns made me wonder what precisely was the nature of her relationship with her husband's brother's best friend. She also seemed to know far too much about Burns's aspirations to achieve a promotion within the Excise, and the machinations to that end in which he had been engaged.

Among the many things I learned about Burns from Maria Riddell was the fact that he had become friendly years before (while he was still at Mossgiel, in fact) with Mrs Frances Dunlop. After the death of her husband in 1785, Mrs Dunlop had become enchanted with Burns's poetry and years of meetings and correspondence ensued, including somewhat terse exchanges about Mrs Dunlop's suggestions for improvements to some poems. It transpired that Mrs Dunlop was a friend of the wife of William Corbet, who at the time was a General Supervisor of the Excise in Scotland, and she had already assisted in securing a promotion for Burns.

On 3rd February Burns wrote to Mrs Dunlop:[4]

Dear Madam

I have just five minutes, less than no time at all to answer your kind letter. Imprimis and in the first place, as to Mr. Corbet, I have some faint hopes of seeing him here this season: if he come, it will be of essential service to me. Not that I have any immediate hopes of a Supervisorship; but there is what is called, a Port Division, here, and, entre nous, the present incumbent is so obnoxious, that Mr. Corbet's presence will in all probability send him adrift into some other Division, and with equal probability will fix me in his stead. A Port Division is twenty pounds a year more than any other Division, beside as much rum and brandy as will easily supply an ordinary family; which last consideration brings me to my second head of discourse, namely your unfortunate hunting of smugglers for a little brandy; an article I believe indeed very scarce in your country.

I have however hunted these gentry to better purpose than you, and as a servant of my brother's goes from here to Mauchline tomorrow morning, I beg leave to send you by him a very small jar, sealed full of as genuine Nantz as ever I tasted. This freedom I hope you will forgive. The jar will reach you, I trust, by some safe channel, though by what channel, I shall leave my brother to direct. Your little Godson sends his most grateful acknowledgements to you. Wilson's book I have not Seen; but will be much obliged to you for a sight of it. My glass is run. A Dieu je vous commende!

Dumfries, 3rd February 1792　　　　　　　　Robt. Burns

Burns followed this up with an appeal direct to Corbet in which he unashamedly sought to use the friendship of Mrs Dunlop and Mrs Corbet as a lever to secure his elevation in the Excise, as his letter shows:[5]

Sir,

I have in my time taken up the pen on several ticklish subjects, but none that ever cost me half so much as the language of Supplication. –To lay open one's wants & woes to the mercy of another's benevolence, is a business so prostituted by the worthless & unfeeling, that a man of Principle & Delicacy shrinks from it as from Contamination.–

Mr Findlater tells me that you wish to know from myself, what are my views in desiring to change ~~situation~~ my Excise Division.–With the wish natural to man, of bettering his present situation, I have turned my thoughts towards the practicality of getting into a Port Division. –As I know that the General Superrs. are omniponent in these matters, my honored friend, Mrs Dunlop of Dunlop, offered me to interest you in my behalf.–She told me that she was well acquainted with Mrs Corbet's goodness, & that on the score of former intimacy, she thought she could promise some influence with her: and added, with her usual sagacity & knowledge of human nature, that the surest road to the good offices of a man was through the meditation of the woman he loved.–On this footing, Sir, I venture my application; else, not even the known generosity of your character would have emboldened me to address you thus.–

I have the honor to be, sir,
your very humble servant
Robt Burns

However unlikely it may seem that such an approach would be successful, Burns did indeed obtain the promotion he desired.

Burns was assiduous in carrying out his duties in the Excise over the next few months, including the seizure of the brig *Rosamond of Plymouth*, abandoned by her smuggler crew in the face of an attack by Burns and his officers. The net proceeds of the vessel and its cargo amounted to £121, half of which benefitted the King. That perhaps led to Burns receiving the honour of being appointed to the King's ceremonial bodyguard, the Royal Archers of Scotland, on 10th April. I was never sure just how pleased he was to receive this commendation, as subsequent events cast some doubt on his commitment to the monarchy, and some of his later writings contain more than a hint of republicanism.

There had been suggestions of a new Edinburgh Edition of Burns's poetry to be published by William Creech in 1791. In fact, Burns seems to have received some misleading information about what Creech was intending because in writing to Peter Hill in October 1791, he had included the following:[6]

My dear Friend,

… By the way, I have taken a damned vengeance on Creech. He wrote me a fine, fair letter, telling me he was going to print a third edition; and, as he had a brother's care of my fame, he wished to add every new thing I have written since, and I should be amply rewarded with – a copy or two to present to my friends! He has sent me a copy of the last edition to correct &c., but I have as yet taken no notice of it, and I hear he has published without me… .

Ellisland, October 1791   R. Burns

This was incorrect, but if Creech was upset about Burns's negligent behaviour, it did not prevent him renewing his approach to Burns in April 1792. To say that Burns's relationship with Creech was up and down is an understatement, because in replying to Creech on 16th April,[7] only a few months after his letter to Peter Hill, Burns strikes a conciliatory, even apologetic, tone:

Sir,

I this moment have yours, and were it not that habit, as usual, has deadened conscience, my criminal indolence should lead me an uneasy life of reproach. I ought long ago to have written you on this very business.

Now, to try a language of which I am not half master, I shall assume, as well as I can, the man of business. I suppose, at a gross guess, that I could add of new materials, to your two volumes, about fifty pages. I would also correct and retrench a good deal. These said fifty pages you know are as much mine as the thumb-stall I have just now drawn on my finger which I unfortunately gashed in mending my pen. A few books which I very much want are all the recompence I crave, together with as many copies of this new edition of my own works as Friendship or Gratitude shall prompt me to present. There are three men whom you know and whose friendly patronage I think I can trouble so far–Messrs McKenzie, D. Stewart, and F. Tytler: to any of these I shall submit my MSS. for their strictures; and also let them say on my informing them –I mean any of them–what Authors I want, to what value of them I am entitled. If he adjudged me a 'Tom Thumb,' I am content. The 'Man of Feeling' and Professor Stewart are, I hear, busy with works of their own, for which reason I shall

186

prefer Tytler. So soon as I hear from you, I shall write Mr Tytler; and in a fortnight more I shall put my MSS. in his hands.

If the thing were possible that I could receive the proof-sheets by our Dumfries Fly, which runs three times a week, I would earnestly wish to correct them myself.

I have the honor to be, Sir,
your very humble servant,

Dumfries, 16th April 1792   Robt. Burns

The 'Man of Feeling' is, of course, Henry Mackenzie. In the event, I did correct the proofs for what became the 1793 Edinburgh Edition, and Burns expressed his thanks in his letter to me of 6th December 1792:[8]

Sir,

A poor caitiff, driving, as I am at this moment with an excise-quill, at the rate of "Devil take the hindmost", is ill-qualified to round the period of gratitude, or swell the pathos of sensibility. Gratitude, like some other amiable qualities of the mind, is nowadays so abused by imposters, that I have sometimes wished that the project of that sly dog Momus, I think it is, had gone into effect–planting a window in the breast of man. In that case, when a poor fellow comes, as I do at this moment, before his benefactor, tongue-tied with the sense of these very obligations, he would have had nothing to do but place himself in front of his friend, and lay bare the workings of his bosom.

I again trouble you with another, and my last, parcel of manuscript. I am not interested in any of these; blot them at your pleasure. I am much indebted to you for taking the trouble of correcting the press-work. One instance, indeed, may be rather unlucky: if the lines to Sir John Whiteford are printed, they ought to end, "And tread the shadowy path to that dark world unknown" "shadowy", instead of, "dreary", as I believe it stands at present. I wish this could be noticed in the Errata. This comes of writing, as I generally do, from the memory.

I have the honor to be, Sir,

Your deeply indebted humble servant,

6th. Decr. 1792   Robt. Burns

In May Burns had occasion to be grateful that he was well connected with the law. I believe he had been celebrating his recent transfer to the Dumfries Port Division with his colleague John Lewars, which brought him additional remuneration. In the early hours of the morning of Saturday 18th May, Burns and Lewars were making their way home from the Globe tavern after a night of heavy drinking. I believe that Lewars was dehydrated and asked for some water from the servant quarters of one of the large houses, but, having been refused, had broken down the door, become abusive and manhandled one of the maids. The fiscal of court was David Newall, Burns's friend and former neighbour at Ellisland. He charged Lewars with assault, but kept Burns out of the case, though he could have been regarded as being involved. In the event, when the case came before the magistrates at the end of the month, Newall, with consent of the magistrates, abandoned the case, perhaps on account of Lewars's position in the Excise.

Around this time there was unrest as the electoral reform movement had again been frustrated by Parliament talking out Richard Sheridan's annual proposals for extension of the franchise.

There were riots throughout the country, effigies of Henry Dundas were burned in various towns, and in Edinburgh, there was chaos for two or three days as a mob smashed windows in the properties of those regarded as the ruling class, including the residences of Dundas and his nephew Robert, the Lord Advocate. On 21st May a Royal Proclamation against seditious writings was promulgated.

All these events led in July to the creation, by those seeking a more democratic system, of the Scottish Association of the Friends of the People. Initially its membership was broad based, and while its aims were reformist, it pledged support for the constitution and loyalty to Great Britain and the King. Among its members were Lord Daer; the minister Thomas Fyshe Palmer; and my fellow advocates Harry Erskine, John Morthland, Thomas Muir and Robert Forsyth.

On 13th August the fourth volume of *The Scots Musical Museum* was published by James Johnson. Burns's contributions included 'Craigieburn Wood' and the haunting 'Ae Fond Kiss', a poem he had composed to mark the end of his relationship with Mrs Agnes McLehose. Shortly after the volume came on sale, Burns received a proposal from George Thomson, a member of the Board of Trustees for the Encouragement of Art and Manufacture in Scotland, for *A Select Collection of Scottish Airs*. Thomson was a friend of my father William Tytler, who was a great supporter of Scottish music throughout his life. My father had suggested that Thomson ask Burns to write twenty to twenty-five songs suitable for the particular melodies which Thomson would provide. Burns was enthusiastic, but in view of what he had told me of the stress he had suffered as a result of his dealings with Creech, I recommended that he enter into a clear and unequivocal contract with Thomson. This he absolutely refused to do, and, against my advice, he wrote to Thomson on 16th September[9] including the following:

Sir

... As to remuneration, you may think my songs either above, or below price; for they shall absolutely be the one or the other. In the honest enthusiasm with which I embark in your undertaking, to talk of money, wages, fee, hire, &c. would be downright sodomy of soul! A proof of each of the songs that I compose or amend, I shall receive as a favor. In the rustic phrase of the Season, "God speed the wark!"

I am, Sir, your very
humble servant

Dumfries, 16th Sept., 1792   Robt. Burns

P.S. I have some particular reasons for wishing my interference to be known as little as possible.

R.B.

It was madness, of course. Burns needed all the money he could get to support his family and himself. This streak of idealism was, to me, the first sign of a kind of instability which gradually overtook him. I later learned that Ignaz Pleyel, the composer of various accompaniments to the Airs, received more than £131 for his contribution. That would have been about two years' remuneration for Burns in the Excise, a fortune which would have alleviated a great deal of the stress and unhappiness of his latter years.

Unfortunately, my father did not live to see the publication of the result of the collaboration between Thomson and Burns as he died in September 1792. My father was, of course, best known for his *The*

Enquiry, Historical and Critical, into the Evidence against Mary Queen of Scots (1760), a defence of Mary for whom he was the leading apologist. In 1787, this had impelled Burns to compose 'Address to Wm Tytler, Esq. of Woodhouselee':[10]

> Revered defender of beauteous Stuart,
> Of Stuart, a name once respected;
> A name which to love was the mark of a true heart,
> But now 'tis despised and neglected.
>
> Tho' something like moisture conglobes in my eye,
> Let no one misdeem me disloyal:
> A poor, friendless wand'rer may well claim a sigh,
> Still more if that wand'rer were royal.
>
> My fathers that name have rever'd on a throne:
> My fathers have fallen to right it;
> Those fathers would spurn their degenerate son
> That name should he scoffingly slight it.
>
> Still in prayers for King George I most heartily join,
> The Queen and the rest of the gentry:
> Be they wise, be they foolish, is nothing of mine,
> Their title's avow'd by my country.
>
> But why of that epocha make such a fuss,
> That gave us th' Electoral stem?
> If bringing them over was lucky for us,
> I'm sure 'twas as lucky for them!
>
> But loyalty, truce! we're on dangerous ground:
> Who knows how the fashions may alter?
> The doctrine today that is loyalty sound,
> Tomorrow may bring us a halter!

I send you a trifle, a head of a bard,
A trifle scarce worthy your care;
But accept it, good Sir, as a mark of regard,
Sincere as a saint's dying prayer.

Now life's chilly evening dim shades on your eye,
And ushers the long dreary night:
But you, like the star that athwart gilds the sky,
Your course to the latest is bright.

In view of his clearly expressed sympathy for Jacobitism in the persona of my father, it was as well that this had been composed well before Burns secured his position in the Excise, though he would have been well advised to heed his own words that politics is dangerous ground. He had previously also expressed support for the American War of Independence, and around this time was indiscreet in his admiration for the French Revolution. I suspected that Burns had great sympathy for the republican movement, but I counselled him to be cautious, not least because he was a government employee.

Unfortunately my advice was ignored. At the conclusion of a play at the Theatre Royal in Dumfries at the end of October, there was a bit of a rumpus between Tory supporters calling for the National Anthem and liberals calling for 'Ca ira!', the revolutionary anthem. Burns seemed to have got caught up in the middle of it, and when I questioned him about it later, he laughed it off, though with a touch of sheepishness.

Burns's daughter Elizabeth Riddell Burns was born in November. He named her after the wife of his friend Captain Robert Riddell. This shows the depth of the friendship between Burns and the Riddell family at that time.

In December a National Convention of the Friends of the People was called in Edinburgh. My fellow advocate Thomas Muir read an address from the Dublin Society of United Irishmen which had overtly nationalist overtones. Acceptance of this address was opposed by Lord Daer and the advocates Erskine, Morthland and Forsyth, but they seemed to be in a minority. Daer later wrote that the Scottish Society was almost unanimously an enemy of the Union with England.

If the sheepishness shown by Burns after the theatre incident betrayed a modicum of concern on his part, it was well founded. On 31st December, Burns was in a terrible state. He was threatened with dismissal from the Excise, as an investigation by his superior collector, John Mitchell, into his political conduct had been initiated.

Later

I was one of the judges in the court which decided the cases brought by Burns's family and Trustees against Thomas Stewart for interdict, and against James Robertson for interdict and damages, both cases in respect of breach of copyright. In the former action, interdict was granted, but in the latter, the pursuers were unsuccessful in Edinburgh. I was in the minority who considered that the copyright had been breached, and damages should have been awarded. Happily, the decision was reversed in 1811 on appeal to the House of Lords, and my view was vindicated.

CHAPTER 15

EMPLOYMENT ISSUES

1793

ALEXANDER CUNNINGHAM

When Burns arrived in Edinburgh in 1786, Alexander Cunningham was twenty-three years old and was working as a lawyer. He was a subscriber to the Edinburgh Edition. He became a Writer to the Signet in 1798, two years after the poet's death. He later went into business as a jeweller in partnership with his uncle.

Burns and Cunningham corresponded regularly after the poet moved to Dumfriesshire. After Burns's death, Cunningham played a major part in raising funds for the poet's family.

Alexander Cunningham died in 1812.

My name is Alexander Cunningham. I am a lawyer by profession. I am forty-seven years of age. I make this statement on 31st October 1810.

I first met Robert Burns in 1786 just after he arrived in Edinburgh. I was introduced to him by Harry Erskine at Lodge Canongate Kilwinning, and for the following fifteen months Robert and I, along with my fellow lawyer Robert Ainslie, had a friendship the like of which I have never since experienced. I was distraught when Robert decided to move to Ellisland, but we kept in touch right up to the end of his life.

In early 1789 I had suffered extreme disappointment when a young lady I had been courting decided to marry a surgeon with, I suspect, better prospects than I had at the time. Robert wrote me a letter of condolence, though it was unnecessarily insensitive of him to include what amounted to a eulogy in praise of matrimony. His sensitivity did come to the fore in his correspondence with me later that year, but it was towards defenceless animals in the poem he sent me in May, 'On seeing a fellow wound a hare with a shot'. He did, however, congratulate me on my later marriage in September 1792.

Over the years, Robert sought my legal assistance on a variety of matters; for example, in February 1791 he asked me to help his friend James Clarke, the Moffat schoolmaster wrongly accused of cruelty towards his pupils and threatened with dismissal from his post. That case was successfully resolved.

Turning to 1793, in January Robert himself was under threat of dismissal. There was an Excise investigation into his conduct, allegations having been made against him that he was the leader of a disaffected faction in Dumfries, that he was a reformer, that he had spoken ill of the monarchy, and that he was a supporter of William Johnston, the founder and publisher of the radical *Gazette* newspaper in Edinburgh. Robert refuted these charges, although I know he was less than frank in many of his denials. For example, although he submitted that he knew nothing of Johnston, only a month earlier he had written to him asking to be added as a subscriber to the *Gazette*, and had encouraged Johnston to expose what he – Robert – described as corruption at the heart of the political administration.

Robert Graham, Commissioner of the Scottish Board of Excise and a long-term patron of Robert, was able to deflect much of the criticism of his protégé, but Robert had been naïve in his defences against the allegations made against him by conceding that his view was that a system of corruption was in existence between the executive power and the representative part of the legislature, which boded no good for what he described as the "glorious Constitution", and which he considered every patriotic Briton must wish to see amended. Graham could not defend that, and the Excise sent William Corbet, a senior officer in Edinburgh, to Dumfries to carry out an on-the-spot investigation. Corbet cleared Robert in the end, but there is no doubt in my mind it put paid to any chance of Robert being promoted within the Excise. Robert told me that Corbet advised him that his business was to act, not to think. Corbet might as well have told Robert not to breathe.

He did, however, largely keep his thoughts on constitutional matters to himself, or at least shared them with close friends only after this scare. For example, when he wrote to me in February, he opened with his usual fine turn of phrase, enquiring if I was "engaged in the mazes of the law, the mysteries of love or in the profound wisdom of politics". This set him off on a description of his jaundiced view of politics and government ministers, the first being "a science wherewith, by means of nefarious cunning and hypocritical pretence, we govern civil politics for the emolument of ourselves and adherents"; and the second – a minister – being "an unprincipled fellow who, by the influence of hereditary or acquired wealth, by superior abilities, or by a lucky conjuncture of circumstances, obtains a principal place in the administration of the affairs of government".[1]

Robert was cautious at this time about revealing his authorship of new works with political overtones. He insisted that anything he wrote for newspapers or periodicals be published under a nom de plume or anonymously.

Robert had initially been an enthusiastic supporter of the French Revolution as he saw it as a move towards democracy replacing the absolute power of the monarchy. He was not, of course, alone in this, and in 1792 there had been widespread circulation of pamphlets supporting reform in Britain. Thomas Paine was the most prominent reformer, having published his book *Rights of Man* in March 1791 and followed it up in March 1792 with *Rights of Man, Part the Second, Combining Principle and Practice.* This had a devastating impact as it detailed how progressive taxation of the rich could alleviate poverty, and the publication provoked the creation of a considerable number of reform societies. The British government panicked in the face of this, and issued a royal proclamation against seditious writing. Paine was then indicted for seditious libel.

Robert was a disciple of Paine; he had copies of *Rights of Man* and also *Common Sense*, Paine's 1776 pamphlet supporting the American War of Independence. In December 1792, when Paine was tried in his absence on the charge of seditious libel, he was defended by the English barrister Thomas Erskine, the younger brother of Robert's friend Harry Erskine, the Dean of the Faculty of Advocates. Paine was convicted, but Robert had been delighted to read the passage in Erskine's speech[2] on the duty of lawyers to defend the rights of the individual:

I will for ever, at all hazards, assert the dignity, independence, and integrity of the English Bar, without which impartial justice, the most valuable part of the English constitution, can have no existence. From the moment that any advocate can be permitted to say that he will or will not stand between the Crown and the subject arraigned in the court where he daily sits to practise, from that moment the liberties of England are at an end.

I consider that the declaration of war by France against Great Britain following the execution of Louis XVI in January 1793 marked a sort of turning point in Robert's attitude to events in France. His hero Paine had settled in France and was a member of the National Convention. Paine had opposed the execution of Louis and strenuously maintained, instead, that he should be exiled to America. Maximilien de Robespierre, President of the National Convention, reacted to this show of dissent with fury, and later in the year Paine was arrested and sentenced to death. He avoided execution only because of the fall and execution of Robespierre himself. Robert was appalled by this sequence of events.

The second Edinburgh Edition of Robert's poems was published in February by William Creech, and Robert received twenty copies for distribution to friends as his sole reward, having previously sold the copyright to Creech. I had encouraged Robert to demand further payment from Creech for the new works included in this edition, but Robert would have none of it. With the benefit of hindsight, it seems even more ludicrous that Robert received absolutely nothing for the composition of 'Tam o' Shanter'.

Robert was concerned for the health of his infant daughter, Elizabeth Riddell Burns, who was a sickly child. In May Robert moved his family from the flat in the Wee Vennel to a house on Mill Hole Brae. While the property was an improvement on the cramped conditions at the flat, there was no corresponding amelioration in Elizabeth's health.

In July my friend John Syme accompanied Robert on a trip round the south-west of Scotland. They lodged with friends who occupied opposite ends of the political spectrum during this sojourn. They stayed at Kenmure Castle, the seat of the Gordon family, with John Gordon. He is a Jacobite sympathiser whose grandfather was William Gordon, 6th Viscount of Kenmure and Lord Lochinvar. In 1715 Viscount Kenmure joined the Jacobite rising and was commander of the Lowland Jacobite forces. Kenmure had unwisely proclaimed King James VIII at Kelso before leading his forces into England as far as Preston where he was captured. He was subsequently tried, found guilty and beheaded on 24th February 1716, and his title and estates forfeited.

Syme and Robert then stayed with the late Dunbar Douglas, 4th Earl of Selkirk, at St Mary's Isle. Selkirk was an intelligent seventy-year-old who had attended the University of Glasgow and been granted the honorary Doctorate of Civil Law. He was a liberal, and had been a supporter of the government during the Jacobite Rising of 1745. While staying with Selkirk, Robert met Pietro Urbani, the Italian singer and composer, and they developed together the words and music of what would become one of Robert's best known compositions, the patriotic 'Scots wha' hae'.

On his return to Dumfries, Robert had to deal with a copyright issue. As a result of an introduction I had made the previous year, Robert had been collaborating with George Thomson, the Edinburgh music publisher, on the production of a collection of songs, and a first edition of the *Select Collection of Scottish Airs* had been published in June. Thomson had sent Robert a copy of the collection along with a five pound note. Robert had previously told Thomson he wanted no payment for his contributions, and he told Thomson he felt insulted by the gesture, though not sufficiently to return the note. He did however warn Thomson not to repeat the gesture.

Thomson did wish to ensure he had the copyright to the collection, so Robert signed a certificate[3] which gave Thomson some protection while reserving to Robert the rights to publish the songs himself:

> I do hereby certify to all those whom it may concern, that all the Songs of my composition, published & to be published along with Scotish airs by M. George Thomson of Edinburgh, are so published by my authority & consent: & in particular, that I never authorised any other person to publish any of those songs which were written by me for his work.
>
> And, only reserving to myself the power of publishing these songs, at any future period, & in any manner I may think proper, I do hereby, as far as I legally can, prohibit any other person than the said George Thomson from publishing the before mentioned Songs, & do also empower him to prosecute in terms of law any person or persons pirating, publishing, or vending the said Songs, or any of them, without his consent; & that at his own expence & for his own behoof.
>
> In witness whereof, I have written & subscribed these presents, at Dumfries, the second day of August, one Thousand, seven Hundred and ninety three years.
>
> Robt. Burns

Robert's relationship with Thomson was always fraught as Thomson was an awkward meddler with Robert's work and was jealous of the bond Robert had with James Johnson. When Robert came to Edinburgh for the first time, he met Johnson, a music engraver who had set up in business on his own account in Bell's Wynd, and Robert had contributed two songs to Johnson's first edition of his *The Scots Musical Museum*. After he moved to Dumfriesshire, Robert acted as de facto editor of the *Museum*, contributing over 150 songs himself and revising the submissions others had made in the further three editions which were published before Robert died. Robert made it clear to Thomson that Johnson was equally entitled to publish his work.

Nothing better illustrates the conflicts of conscience which troubled liberal thinkers at this time than the Thomas Muir affair. After being sent down from the University of Glasgow as a firebrand agitator, Muir secured a place at the Faculty of Law at the University of Edinburgh and was then admitted to the Faculty of Advocates in 1787. He became a leading light in the Scottish Reform movement, but came into conflict with Robert's friend Harry Erskine. As is well known, Erskine was a proponent of limited electoral reform, but he was opposed to annual parliaments and universal male suffrage, so he disapproved of the aims of the Scottish Association of the Friends of the People championed by Muir. This Association formed alliances with other reform movements, including the United Irishmen, and held a Convention when Muir propounded Scottish separatist sentiments. Eventually Muir was arrested and charged with seditious practices, including a charge that he feloniously exhorted several persons to purchase and peruse works by Thomas Paine. After being released on bail in early January 1793, he had travelled to Paris to support Paine in his attempt to persuade the National Convention to spare the life of Louis XVI. He was then caught up in the declaration of war and was unable to return to Scotland in time for his trial, so on 25th February, the High Court pronounced a sentence of fugitation against him. That prompted Harry Erskine to convene a meeting of the Faculty of Advocates on 6th March when Muir's name was expunged from the list of the Faculty. Robert was very upset that his friend had taken this step against Muir, as he secretly sympathised with many, although not all, of Muir's aims.

I am sure that Robert was involved in the Dumfries Branch of the Friends of the People which had sent a delegate to Muir's Convention. Muir was arrested on his return to Scotland and tried before the High Court of Justiciary. This is our supreme criminal court, and comprises the Lord Justice General (an hereditary post vested in the Dukes of Argyll), the Lord Justice Clerk, and up to five Lords Commissioner of Justiciary from among the senators of the College of Justice.

Muir was tried at the end of August before Lord Justice Clerk Braxfield and Lords Swinton, Henderland, Dunsinnan and Abercromby. The Lord Advocate, Robert Dundas, led for the Crown, and Muir defended himself. That he was convicted by the jury was no surprise, as Braxfield advised them in his summing up, before the jury decided its verdict, that the accused was poisoning the minds of the common people, and preparing them for rebellion.

What was a surprise was the sentence: fourteen years' transportation. Robert was horrified, and immediately secreted his copies of Paine's works with a trusted neighbour.

More was to follow. In September, Thomas Fyshe Palmer, a Unitarian preacher, was accused of wickedly and feloniously (a) writing or printing, and (b) circulating a seditious writing. He was tried at the High Court on circuit in Perth before Lords Eskgrove and Abercromby, with the prosecution being led by John Burnett assisted by Allan Maconachie. Fyshe Palmer's counsel were John Clerk and John Haggart. Fyshe Palmer was convicted and sentenced to seven years' transportation.

That Robert was much exercised by the prosecutions and convictions of Muir and Fyshe Palmer is shown by what he wrote the following year in his 'Epistle from Esopus to Maria'.[4] The first four lines from the excerpt refer to Maitland Bushby, son of John Bushby, who had been admitted to the Faculty of Advocates but of whom Robert had a poor opinion. The second four lines betray Robert's concerns:

> The hopeful youth, in Scottish senate bred,
> Who owns a Bushby's heart without the head,
> Comes 'mid a string of coxcombs to display
> That Veni, vidi, vici, is his way;
> The shrinking Bard adown the alley skulks
> And dreads a meeting worse than Woolwich hulks,
> Though there his heresies in Church and State
> Might well award him Muir and Palmer's fate.

Later in the year, the Society of the Friends of the People, the organisation seeking political reform, had arranged a meeting in Edinburgh. It came to be known as the 'British Convention of the Delegates of the People, Associated to obtain Universal Suffrage, and Annual Parliaments', and its leaders were William Skirving, a local farmer, and Joseph Gerrald and Maurice Margarot, delegates from England. They issued a manifesto demanding universal male suffrage with annual elections. The Convention was broken up by the authorities, and its leaders arrested. This added to Robert's concerns about expressing his opinions on reform.

I was involved in an unfortunate exchange in November involving Urbani, who had assured me that he had got Robert's agreement to collaborate fully with him, whereas Robert was adamant that while Urbani had permission to use anything Robert had contributed to the *The Scots Musical Museum*, beyond that Robert would not give him any assistance.

Captain Robert Riddell was probably Robert's best friend in the latter part of 1793, and Robert was a frequent guest at Friar's Carse, the Captain's country house. It was there that Robert had met the Captain's sister-in-law Maria, the wife of his younger brother, Walter. Maria fancied herself a writer, and it was not long before an intense friendship developed with Robert. In December 1793 that friendship, and Robert's association with the Riddells of Friar's Carse came to an abrupt end.

Walter Riddell was abroad at the time, so Maria was unaccompanied at a dinner party at Friar's Carse. The *froideur* between Robert and the Riddells was a result of some tomfoolery at this party. Local gossip had it that the Captain had plied Robert with an excess of alcohol during dinner, and when the gentlemen withdrew for port and cigars, the conversation among them turned to a discussion of the painting 'The Rape of the Sabine Women'. Some of the gentlemen, anxious to take Robert down a peg or two, persuaded him to participate in a re-enactment of the scene, and each gentleman was allocated a lady to be the target of his attack. I understand all the gentlemen promised to join in the fun, but when Robert charged into the drawing room and embraced Maria, they remained at the door, pretending to be horrified onlookers. Precisely what Robert did to Maria was never established, but it was sufficient for the Captain to order him out of the house.

Although Robert begged for forgiveness, the Captain and his wife severed all connection with him. Maria Riddell was persuaded to cut Robert from her circle of friends, although she and Robert did have a reconciliation of sorts after the Captain's death in 1794.

As the year 1793 ended, Robert's life was settled. His family was in comfortable accommodation, his work with the Excise was no longer exacting, he had seen off the attempt to have him dismissed, and he had secured burgess privileges for his children at the school in Dumfries. His flirtations with the Riddells had come to a halt, but he still had his Masonic brothers, his professional friends – the local lawyers Samuel Clark and William McCraken, and Doctors James Mundell and William Maxwell – and his drinking companions in the Globe tavern, so the future of both social and business life seemed secure. His boldness in expressing his reformist views had been curbed, and to the wider world it seemed that he did, indeed, regard ballad-making as his 'hobby horse', as he put it. Unfortunately, when he was in drink, that caution tended to be thrown to the winds.

Later

A Petition was presented to Parliament describing the treatment of Muir and others as "illegal, unjust, oppressive and unconstitutional". But these efforts failed and on 2nd May 1794, Muir was embarked for his transportation to the penal colony of Botany Bay. After two years he escaped, and after various escapades (during which he sustained serious injuries), he returned to France where he was reunited with Thomas Paine. Muir never fully recovered from his injuries and he died on 26th January 1799 at the age of thirty-three. Fyshe Palmer served out his full sentence in New South Wales and set off on his return to Great Britain in 1800, but he was detained en route in Guam as a prisoner of war of Spain, and he died there in 1802.

Muir got his vicarious revenge on Harry Erskine in 1796 when Erskine lost the post of Dean of the Faculty of Advocates. An ode in mock consolation of Erskine was composed by the Reverend George Hamilton but attributed to Muir, from whom it nominally came.

Robert asked me to beg the Commissioners of Excise to grant

him his full salary as an exciseman during his last illness, but I think the records show that they treated him quite fairly. Robert was inclined to exaggeration. Shortly before his death, Robert was taking the waters at the village of Brow near Dumfries, and he wrote to me two weeks before his death, telling me that Jean's forthcoming delivery would be named Alexander Cunningham Burns after me if he were a boy; that was left unfulfilled, as the poor boy was named Maxwell by Jean, in honour of Robert's doctor, William Maxwell. Robert also said in that letter that he feared that the Bard was not long to be heard among us. Sadly, that was no exaggeration.

After Robert's death I did what I could to assist Mrs Burns and the family, but most of the burden fell on John Syme before Doctor James Currie assumed control of the literary legacy for the benefit of the family.

CHAPTER 16

TREASON?

1794

SAMUEL CLARK

Samuel Clark was a lawyer in Dumfries and Conjunct Commissary Clerk and Clerk of the Peace for the County.

He was a Freemason and one of the locals in Dumfries who resurrected Lodge St Michael Dumfries in 1789 on a Petition to Alexander Fergusson of Craigdarroch, the Provincial Grand Master. He became Secretary and Clerk to that Lodge. In 1793 the poet officiated when Clark was admitted a member of Lodge St Andrew Dumfries.

Clark was a liberal but enlisted with the poet in the Royal Dumfries Volunteers.

My name is Samuel Clark. I am a lawyer. I am thirty-seven years of age. I make this statement on 31st October 1806. Robert Burns and I became friends after he moved from Ellisland into Dumfries, although I had met him previously through Masonic connections. We were regulars in the Globe tavern; Robert was an entertaining fellow drinker. It would be wrong to suggest that he warmed to the legal profession; in fact, he often expressed his contempt for lawyers, reserving particular opprobrium for the Faculty of Advocates in Edinburgh. He described the Dean of Faculty, Harry Erskine, as a quondam friend in view of the part he had played in the expulsion of the liberal activist Thomas Muir from the Faculty. Robert later recanted that opinion when Erskine himself was badly treated by the Faculty by being removed from the post of Dean in 1796. That reinforced his contempt for the conservative element at the Faculty and, in particular, for all members of the Dundas family.

I knew all about Robert's history with women, so it had been no surprise when, in 1791, Anna Park, my favourite barmaid at the Globe tavern, got pregnant by Robert and produced a daughter. It was sad that Anna left the area, but I know that the daughter, called Betty, is being well looked after by the Burns family. It is a most irregular arrangement.

My father, also a lawyer, was a great admirer of Robert's poems, and when I was in my late teens, of an evening he often recited his favourites from his copy of the Edinburgh Edition. Needless to say, having heard them so many times, I was not too enamoured of them; I found most rather sentimental, though I would never have said that to Robert.

I was a regular visitor to Robert's house in Mill Hole Brae. It is a misconception that Robert and his family were impoverished. Robert and Jean were generous hosts and were in many ways the envy of their neighbours in that they always had a maidservant and seldom would a week pass by than some gift of fresh produce would be delivered to them from the country. I think these gifts were made partly in recognition of Robert as a local worthy, but also partly to ensure the continuation of harmonious relationships with the Excise. I put it no higher than that.

Early in 1794, the sedition trials continued, greatly troubling Robert. In January William Skirving was convicted and sentenced by Lord Justice Clerk Braxfield and Lords Eskgrove, Swinton, Dunsinnan and Abercromby to fourteen years' transportation, the same punishment as the advocate Thomas Muir had received in 1793. Then came news of the outcome of the case against Maurice Margarot who was tried by the Lord Justice Clerk and Lords Eskgrove, Swinton, Henderland and Dunsinnan. The prosecution was led by the Lord Advocate; Margarot defended himself. He raised numerous objections to the proceedings, all of which were repelled. He then sought to call the Lord Justice Clerk as a witness, but was required to detail the questions he wished to put to Braxfield. It transpired that Margarot had heard about certain views allegedly expressed by Braxfield about the case, and his questions were as follows:[1]

> Did you dine at Mr Rochead's at Inverleith in the course of last week?

> Did any conversation take place with regard to my trial?

> Did you use these words: What should you think of giving him a hundred lashes, together with Botany Bay? Or words to that purpose?

> Did any person, did a lady, say to you that the mob would not allow you to whip him? And, my Lord, did you not say that the mob would be better for losing a little blood?

Margarot challenged Braxfield to deny the questions or acknowledge them, but Braxfield was too wily for him. He turned to the other four judges and asked them to say whether he should answer questions of that sort. Unsurprisingly, they unanimously refused to allow Margarot to put the questions to Braxfield. One might think that just hearing the questions would be enough to cause the members of the jury to doubt Braxfield's impartiality but he was unconcerned, and when Margarot had completed his closing speech to the jury, and before summing up, he advised them that Margarot's speech had been sedition from beginning to end.

Margarot was convicted on 14th January and received the sentence of fourteen years' transportation. No whipping was imposed as part of the punishment.

Gerrald was tried in March before the same Court. He lodged a Minute with the Court objecting to the Lord Justice Clerk as a judge, citing the views that Braxfield was alleged to have expressed and referred to in Margarot's trial. This time Braxfield left the chair and Lord Henderland and the others each repelled the objection in turn, Eskgrove feigning his inability to perceive Gerrald's motive for making it. Without a blush, Eskgrove observed that Gerrald "will … be treated as an innocent man, till he is found guilty".[2]

Robert Blair, the Solicitor General, prosecuted the case. Gerrald was represented by John Clerk, Malcolm Laing, Archibald Fletcher and Adam Gillies. Although Gillies was only twenty-eight years old, he led the defence. One of the jury panel who had been selected was William Creech, Robert's Edinburgh publisher, and Gillies objected to him on the ground that he had repeatedly declared that he would condemn any member of the British Convention if he should be called to pass on their assize. The objection was repelled, with Braxfield, true to form, trenchantly averring that he hoped that there was not a gentleman on the jury, or any man in the Court, who had not expressed the same sentiment, and adding, once again interrupting Gerrald's submissions to the jury, that everything he was saying was sedition.

All these cases, involving as they did people well known to Robert, some of whom he had previously respected, contributed to periods of low spirits Robert suffered from around this time, and he was prone to sink into melancholy reminiscing about happier times in Edinburgh. He described these periods of tristesse as occurring when his heart was in a wandering humour, and the visages of those drinking companions from his past such as William Dunbar, Alexander Cunningham and William Smellie presented themselves to him. It is fair to say that the effect of strong drink also played a part in these episodes.

Through my father's connections, I had got to know William Corbet, the Supervisor of Excise. During a rather inebriated discussion with Robert in the spring of 1794, I foolishly mentioned this. Robert had, of course, been cleared of misconduct in the Excise by William the previous year, but he was still nervous about his prospects for promotion, as is clear from this extract from his letter to me:[3]

> My dear Sir,
>
> I recollect something of a drunken promise yesternight to breakfast with you this morning. I am very sorry that it is impossible. I remember too, you very obligingly mentioning something of your intimacy with Mr Corbet, our Supervisor-General. Some of our folks about the Excise Office, Edinburgh, had, and perhaps still have, conceived a prejudice against me as being a drunken dissipated character. I might be all this, you know, and yet be an

honest fellow; but you know that I am an honest fellow, and am nothing of this. You may in your own way let him know that I am not unworthy of subscribing myself, my dear Clark, your friend,

R. Burns

I do know that Robert had proposed some restructuring of the Excise in Dumfries, and had hoped for promotion. He had got hold of the idea that his superior, Alexander Findlater, was about to be promoted, and canvassed his patron Robert Graham of Fintry in the hope of getting Findlater's job. That never happened, save that Robert stood in for Findlater when he was ill later in the year.

At this time, Great Britain's involvement in the French Revolutionary War had been going on for about eighteen months. When Robert was the worse for wear he could be scathing about what he regarded as an unjust and unnecessary conflict. In business circles he was careful to keep his opinions to himself, but Dumfries had seen a huge influx of the military because of its strategic position. The town was garrisoned by first the Strathspey Fencibles, then the Royal Ulster Volunteers and latterly, the Cinque Ports Cavalry. On a few occasions, I had to quieten Robert when he threatened to become involved in arguments with officers and other ranks.

In one incident Robert tried to be too clever by half in proposing a toast to Great Britain's success in the War. His wording was clearly ambiguous: "May our success in the present war be equal to the justice of our cause."[4] I found that rather perceptive, but it provoked outrage from the military present at the function. I thought nothing of it, and was surprised to receive a letter[5] from Robert the next day:

215

TREASON?

Dr. Sir

I was, I know, drunk last night, but I am sober this morning. From the expressions Capt. Dods made use of to me, had I had nobody else's welfare to care for but my own, we should certainly have come, according to the manners of the world, to the necessity of murdering one another about the business. The words were such as, generally, I believe, end in a brace of pistols; but I am still pleased to think that I did not ruin the peace and welfare of a wife and a family in a drunken squabble. Farther you know that the report of certain political opinions being mine, has already once before brought me to the brink of destruction. I dread last night's business may be misrepresented in the same way. YOU, I beg, will take care to prevent it. I tax your wish for Mr Burns's welfare with the task of waiting as soon as possible, on every gentleman who was present, and state this to him, and, as you please, shew him this letter. What, after all, was the obnoxious toast? 'May our success in the present war be equal to the justice of our cause'–a toast that the most outrageous frenzy of loyalty cannot object to. I request and beg that this morning you will wait on the parties present at the foolish dispute. I shall only add that I am truly sorry that a man who stood so high in my estimation as Mr Dods should use me in the manner in which I conceive he has done.

I am, Dr.Sir,
yours sincerely,

Sunday Morning   R.B.

Once again he revealed his lack of confidence in his position at the Excise. Captain Dods was from Dunscore, so to reassure Robert, I rode out to have a word with him. He feigned to remember nothing of the incident and, when I asked if that was the end of the matter, he told me it was forgotten. In the event, there were no repercussions for Robert.

In April 1794 Captain Robert Riddell, Robert's erstwhile best friend in Dumfries, died at the age of thirty-nine. They had become estranged following a notorious incident involving misbehaviour by Robert at a dinner party a few months previously. Robert composed 'Sonnet on the death of Robert Riddell',[6] a tribute to his erstwhile friend:

> No more, ye warblers of the wood, no more,
> Nor pour your descant grating on my soul!
> Thou young-eyed Spring, gay in thy verdant stole,
> More Welcome were to me grim Winter's wildest roar!
>
> How can ye charm, ye flowers, with all your dyes?
> Ye blow upon the sod that wraps my friend.
> How can I to the tuneful strain attend?
> That strain flows round th' untimely tomb where Riddell lies.
>
> Yes, pour, ye warblers, pour the notes of woe,
> And sooth the Virtues weeping o'er his bier!
> The man of worth – and "hath not left his peer!"–
> Is in his "narrow house", for ever darkly low.
>
> Thee, Spring, again with joy shall others greet;
> Me, memory of my loss will only meet.

Robert was fascinated by the intrigue which followed the Captain's death. The Captain had no children. He had transferred his estate to trustees, and directed that his wife Elizabeth should have a life interest until her death, and that then the estate capital should pass to his brothers Walter and Alexander in such proportions as should be decided by his widow, even if this meant that one brother was excluded from inheriting.

There was disagreement as to what should happen to Friar's Carse, and Robert somehow got inside information about the arrangements for a potential sale. He had befriended John McLeod of Coldbeck, who was interested in purchasing the property, and, in the face of my advice to him not to get involved, wrote to John on 18th June advising that: the trustees had instructed the factor and manager for Mr Menteith of Closeburn (one William Stewart, "my most intimate friend") to value the estate; that Stewart had promised him a copy of the valuation; and that he could provide John with "underhand intelligence" about how much would be necessary to secure the property. This was sharp practice, uncharacteristic of him and quite unworthy, but happily John decided not to offer.

In the event, Friar's Carse was sold to Doctor Peter Smith for £15,000, and the widow Riddell moved to Edinburgh. She appointed the capital of her late husband's estate to Alexander, but Walter prevailed upon him to divide the estate equally on their sister-in-law's death in 1801.

Robert was always very unkind about Walter. Part of the reason for this was his infatuation with Walter's wife Maria, who was abandoned for long periods in Dumfriesshire while Walter was on what were alleged to be mercantile voyages to the West Indies. Walter and Maria had moved from London some time before, but Walter's finances were always in a shambles and in fact I do not think he ever completed the purchase of Woodley Park. He had to sell it at a loss of some £3,000 after putting it on the market in April, shortly before the death of the Captain. He signed various trust deeds for his creditors over the years, and I do not think he ever received any financial benefit from the Captain's estate himself before his death in 1802.

Walter was given harsh treatment in verse by Robert in his 'Epitaph for Mr Walter Riddell':[7]

> So vile was poor Wat, such a miscreant slave,
> That the worms ev'n damn'd him when laid in the grave.
> "In his skull there's a famine!" a starved reptile cries;
> "And his heart, it is poison!" another replies.

As Maria Riddell had been an intimate friend of Robert's before the incident at Friar's Carse which caused the rift with the Captain and his wife, it hurt him deeply to be snubbed by Maria. He did not spare her at this time, and while passing her carriage one day he was inspired to craft the following epigram entitled 'Pinned to Mrs Walter Riddell's Carriage':[8]

> If you rattle along like your mistress's tongue,
> Your speed will outrival the dart;
> But, a fly for your load, you'll break down on the road,
> If your stuff be as rotten's her heart.

In March Robert received the offer of a post in London on the literary staff of the *Morning Chronicle*. This came from the editor James Perry by way of Patrick Miller Junior, the Whig Member of Parliament for Dumfries and son of Robert's former landlord at Ellisland. It must have been a tempting offer, because the work expected was pretty minimal and the remuneration considerably more than he was then receiving. Robert was hesitant to accept the post. He told me that he was worried about his commitments to his family, and decided to forego the prospect of additional salary and free time for composition in favour of the security afforded by the Excise. I know that Walter Scott is of the opinion that Robert had a natural dislike of regular labour of a literary kind, and while that may also be a reason why Robert turned down the opportunity, it is far from clear how Scott makes that assessment, since he never met Robert except as a child. Robert did, however, contribute to the Whig newspaper – his controversial poem 'Scots wha' hae' was published in the *Morning Chronicle* on 8th May.

The extent to which Robert was downhearted at this time can be seen from David McCulloch's story about what happened on the King's birthday in June. David, a brother Freemason of Robert's at Lodge St Andrew Dumfries, was on his way to a celebratory ball in company with other revellers when he saw Robert on the other side of the street. He crossed over and asked Robert to join the party. Robert's reply was "Nay, nay, my young friend. That's all over now."[9] David was taken aback, and Robert realised he had been impolite. So he invited David back to his home where they had a few drinks before David went off to the ball.

Robert arranged for David to accompany him later in the month when he visited Patrick Heron at Kirroughtree, near Newton Stewart. Heron was a Whig with political ambitions, and Robert was seeking his patronage, having guessed – correctly as it turned out – that Heron would be elected Member of Parliament for the Stewartry of Kirkcudbright at the next election. Robert's support for Heron was later to generate some witty verses.

In July Robert was amused to learn that his Edinburgh publisher, William Creech, was embroiled in a dispute in which he was being accused of sharp practice bordering on dishonesty in his dealings with one of his authors. John Thomson was a Naval Officer at Leith who in 1768 had published a book on calculations entitled *Thomson's Interest Tables*. The fifth edition of Thomson's book had been printed and sold to Creech and an associate in 1788. By 1793, demand for Thomson's *Interest Tables* was still high in London, but the 1788 edition could not be bought, as it had apparently sold out. Thomson was encouraged to produce a further edition, which he did on his own account, for sale through Robert's friend Peter Hill in Edinburgh. This sale was interdicted by Creech, alleging that he still had 1,546 copies of the 1788 edition to sell, and that for Thomson to publish a new edition before all copies of the previous edition were sold was contrary to the bona fides of the original deal. Robert guffawed when he heard that Creech was claiming someone else was in bad faith!

Thomson was alleging that Creech had, in fact, deliberately withheld his copies of the 1788 edition from the public, as he had published an edition of a rival book, *Tables of Interest by John Morison, Accountant,* which, since he had a direct financial interest in the publication, was more profitable to him than Thomson's *Interest Tables*. John Clerk, Thomson's advocate, described Creech's conduct as "playing his double game". Robert rejoiced in the revelations of Creech's evasiveness and duplicity.

In September came the terrible news of the convictions of Robert Watt and David Downie for treason. After the breaking up of the meetings of the British Convention held in Edinburgh in December 1793, Watt, a wine merchant, and Downie, a goldsmith, had decided that reform would not be achieved by peaceful means, and created a plan for the overthrow of the government. To this end they procured the manufacture of some pikes.

Their plan was hare-brained. A co-ordinated uprising in major cities would take place. In Edinburgh a fire was to be started in the

Excise Office to draw soldiers from the Castle; banks and offices were to be taken, and all judges and magistrates seized. The King was to be ordered to dismiss Parliament and elections with universal suffrage would take place.

They were arrested in May and tried for treason by a Court of Oyer and Terminer, a commission established by the Treason Act of 1708. At their trials in September, the Crown was represented by Robert Dundas, the Lord Advocate; Robert Blair, the Solicitor General; and John Anstruther. Robert Hamilton and William Erskine acted for Watt and Robert Cullen and John Clerk for Downie. The commission included the Lord President Ilay Campbell, the Lord Justice Clerk Braxfield, and Lords Eskgrove, Swinton, Dunsinnan and Abercromby. Both Watt and Downie were convicted, and the Lord President handed down the terrible sentence, describing it as a painful duty:[10]

> The Court doth adjudge, that you, and each of you, to be drawn upon a hurdle to the place of execution, that you be there hanged by the neck, but not until you are dead; and that being alive, you, and each of you, be cut down, and your bowels cut out, and burnt before your face. That each of you heads be severed from your bodies; and your bodies divided into four parts; and that your heads and quarters be disposed of as the King shall think fit: And so the Lord have mercy on your souls.

Downie's sentence was later commuted to banishment from the British dominions, but Watt's commutation was merely to being hung and then decapitated, which took place on 15th October. I believe the execution was a more sombre affair than the execution of Deacon Brodie six years earlier.

Robert was never long without female companionship, and he soon found a replacement for Maria Riddell. When he was at Ellisland he had befriended William Lorimer, a farmer from Craigieburn who had taken another of Patrick Miller of Dalswinton's farms on lease. Kemmishall lay fairly close to Ellisland, and Robert had observed Lorimer's daughter Jean growing up, as he was a frequent visitor to Lorimer's farms in connection with his Excise duties. I can confirm that she was a beautiful young girl, admired by all the bachelors – and married men – who saw her. In 1791 Robert described the sixteen-year-old in 'Craigieburn Wood',[11] when promoting the suit of John Gillespie, one of his colleagues in the Excise:

> Sweet closes the evening on Craigieburn wood,
> And blythely awaukens the morrow;
> But the pride of the spring in the Craigieburn wood
> Can yield me nothing but sorrow.
>
> I see the spreading leaves and flowers,
> I hear the wild birds singing;
> But pleasure they hae nane for me,
> While care my heart is wringing.
>
> I can na tell, I maun na tell,
> I daur na for your anger;
> But secret love will break my heart,
> If I conceal it langer.
>
> I see thee gracefu', straight and tall,
> I see thee sweet and bonie;
> But Oh, what will my torment be,
> If thou refuse thy Johnie!

To see thee in another's arms,
In love to lie and languish,
'Twad be my dead, that will be seen,
My heart wad burst wi' anguish.

But Jeanie, say thou wilt be mine,
Say thou loes nane before me;
And a' my days o' life to come
I'll gratefully adore thee.

To our astonishment, in 1793 Jean Lorimer eloped to Gretna Green when she was only eighteen with a ne'er-do-well called Andrew Whelpdale, but he rapidly abandoned her. She moved back to Craigieburn and reverted to using her maiden name. Robert now cast off the role of agent for his colleague and pursued her himself. I think his conduct was reprehensible in view of her tender years. But Robert, as always, was unapologetic when it came to the opposite sex, regarding any and all women as fair game. He wrote a new version of 'Craigieburn Wood' in 1794, adding the following new verse:[12]

Sweet fa's the eve on Craigleburn.
And blythe awakes the morrow;
But a' the pride o' Spring's return
Can yield me nocht but sorrow.

I see the flowers and spreading trees,
I hear the wild birds singing;
But what a weary wight can please,
And Care his bosom is wringing!

Fain, fain would I my griefs impart,
Yet dare na for your anger;

But secret love will break my heart,
If I conceal it langer.

If thou refuse to pity me,
If thou shalt love another,
When yon green leaves fade frae the tree.
Around my grave they'll wither.

Writing to his publisher, George Thomson, about Jean Lorimer on 19th October, [13] he said:

> The lady on whom it was made, is one of the finest women in Scotland; and, in fact (entre nous), is in a manner to me what Sterne's Eliza was to him – a Mistress, or Friend, or what you will, in the guileless simplicity of Platonic love.

Robert composed about twenty-four songs dedicated to Jean Lorimer (whom he named 'Chloris' during the time of his affair with her), but relations between them tailed off towards the end of 1794. It was no coincidence that this cooling of ardour coincided with a rapprochement between Robert and Maria Riddell.

While he celebrated the birth of his son James Glencairn Burns that year, Robert was still generally very low in spirits. He still yearned for contact from his former Edinburgh connections. He was especially disappointed in Robert Ainslie, the Writer to the Signet, who had become distant, forgetting all the fine times they had enjoyed together. Robert knew that he was a close friend of his former inamorata, Agnes McLehose, and speculated that that might be the reason Ainslie had withdrawn from corresponding with him as a friend. He described a letter from Ainslie as being like something Ainslie would send to a client.

I suppose it was unsurprising that Robert was disappointed by the events of the previous few years. His high hopes for political reform in Great Britain had been dashed, and he often produced his copy of the first Edinburgh Edition, going over those of his subscribers who had been involved in the sedition and treason trials as judges, prosecutors and defence counsel. On the list were the judges Lord President Ilay Campbell, Lord Justice Clerk Braxfield and Lords Abercromby, Dunsinnan, Eskgrove and Swinton, and Crown counsel Anstruther, Blair and Robert Dundas. Robert was ashamed to have been associated with them.

Later

I enlisted with Robert and other liberal-minded men in the Royal Dumfries Volunteers, and was part of the firing party at Robert's funeral.

Of the five convicted of sedition (Muir, Skirving, Margarot, Fyshe Palmer and Gerrald), only Margarot survived his banishment to return home. He died in 1815.

CHAPTER 17

THE BITER BIT

1795

ALEXANDER YOUNG OF HARBURN WS

In the Preface to *Memoirs of Sir Walter Scott, Bart.*, J.G. Lockhart, Scott's son-in-law, acknowledged the assistance he had received in their compilation from Sandie Young who he described as a "steady and esteemed friend" of Sir Walter.

Young was a landowner and a highly regarded lawyer. He had been an apprentice to Scott's father. His politics, as might be expected from his close association with Scott, were conservative and he acted as election agent for Tory candidates.

He was also a director of the Bank of Scotland, retiring in 1814. When Scott's financial difficulties began to unravel, he was recalled by the bank and was instrumental in negotiating the settlement eventually reached with Scott's creditors.

He regarded Burns with suspicion for his liberal views.

My name is Sandie Young. I am a lawyer. I am forty-seven years of age. I make this statement on 31st March 1806. I first met Robert Burns in Edinburgh in 1787. I was in practice as a lawyer in Edinburgh, having been admitted as a Writer to the Signet on 7th March 1786.

One of my most important clients was William Nicol, the Classics Master at the High School and one of the greatest Latin scholars of the age. Burns met Nicol and they quickly became drinking companions. I used to join in their bandying extempore translations of Scots, English and Latin. At that time, I thought Nicol a far greater poet and genius than Burns.

Burns was, of course, a notorious womaniser and, in my view, a drunkard unduly indulged by his employers in the Excise. I was always puzzled by the friendship he was accorded by people I would have expected to avoid him. I know that when Burns moved to Ellisland, my former school classmate, the late Captain Robert Riddell, had befriended him, but it came as no surprise to me that the friendship had terminated before Riddell's death as a result of what I understand was quite outrageous behaviour by Burns towards Riddell's sister-in-law Maria Riddell, although I believe that the lady involved was not entirely blameless in the affair. Having said all that, though I did not admire Burns as a man, I did come to consider him a gifted poet.

At the beginning of 1795 Burns's supervisor in the Excise, Alexander Findlater, was ill and Burns had been appointed acting supervisor on a temporary basis. This was well beyond his capabilities, and the greatly increased workload may have contributed to the failure of his health and his eventual death the next year. Burns's additional remuneration from his temporary post was not sufficient to ease the financial problems he was experiencing at the time, due to the general downturn in trade caused by the hostilities with France and his consequent remuneration in the Excise. I know that he often found himself short of funds, and he borrowed repeatedly; for example, he had to beg three guineas from his friend William Stewart, the land agent and valuer, just to pay his rent to his landlord, John Hamilton.

It was around this time that Burns's long-term friendship with his patron Mrs Frances Dunlop, the widow of John Dunlop of Dunlop, came to an end. Mrs Dunlop is one of the many who indulged Burns, being excessively tolerant of his republican sympathies. Burns had initially been critical of the decision to execute Louis XVI and Marie Antoinette, though I consider that this was tactical in that, like the other radicals Paine and Muir, he thought that the reaction to the barbarity would harm the reform movement in Great Britain. In a letter to Mrs Dunlop, written in January 1795, he referred to the late King of France and his consort as "a perjured blockhead and an unprincipled prostitute".[1] This was the last straw as far as Mrs Dunlop was concerned. Her family has been deeply affected by the French Revolution and the consequential wars. Five of her family were army officers, her daughter Susan was the widow of a French gentleman, and her other daughter, Agnes, was married to a French Royalist refugee. It is hardly surprising that she took such deep offence that she never again communicated with Burns until he was on his deathbed.

In his letter Burns also records his encouragement by reason of news of the outcome of treason trials in London, which were in sharp contrast to the Edinburgh trials. Thomas Hardy, the founder of the London Corresponding Society; John Horne Tooke, the novelist; and John Thelwall of the Society of Friends of the People, had all recently been acquitted. Burns commented:[2]

Thank God, these London trials have given us a little more breath, & I imagine that the time is not far distant when a man may freely blame Billy Pitt, without being called an enemy to his Country.

Burns greatly admired the poem composed by Coleridge[3] in praise of Thomas Erskine, brother of his friend Harry Erskine. Thomas Erskine had successfully defended Hardy, Tooke and Thelwall.

> When British Freedom for a happier land
> Spread her broad wings, that flutter'd with affright,
> ERSKINE! thy voice she heard, and paus'd her flight
> Sublime of hope! For dreadless thou didst stand
> (Thy censer glowing with the hallow'd flame)
> An hireless Priest before th' insulted shrine,
> And at her altar pourd'st the stream divine
> Of unmatch'd eloquence. There thy name
> Her sons shall venerate, and cheer thy breast
> With blessings heaven-ward breath'd. And when the doom
> Of Nature bids thee die, beyond the tomb
> Thy light shall shine: as sunk beneath the West
> Tho' the great Summer Sun eludes our gaze,
> Still burns wide Heaven with his distended blaze.

Burns was continuing to compose material for the music publisher George Thomson, including the now famous 'A Man's a Man', which reinforced the suspicions of many that he harboured republican sentiments. I personally think that the composition is given too much credit, as Burns's experience of the world was limited in the extreme. If he had been so concerned about humanity, he would surely have been prominent in promoting the abolition of slavery, whereas he had actually contemplated emigration to Jamaica as a young man to be an overseer in slave plantations. That might be forgiven due to his youth, but in his later life he was silent on the matter, apart from his rather uninspiring 'Slave's Lament' which appeared in 1792. Burns must have been well aware of the issue, for the Church of Scotland took a leading role in the matter, and the advocates Allan Maconachie and John Maclaurin (later Lords Meadowbank and Dreghorn), both subscribers to the first Edinburgh Edition, were counsel for the negro slave Joseph Knight in the famous case of *Wedderburn* v. *Knight*.[4] In that case, the justices at Perth had found that Sir John Wedderburn was entitled to Joseph's service as a slave. On appeal to the Sheriff, the judgment was recalled, and the Sheriff (John Swinton, later Lord Swinton) declared that the state of slavery was not recognised in Scotland, and was inconsistent with the principles of Scots Law. Wedderburn now appealed, but his appeal was dismissed by a majority, the dissenting judges being Lord President Robert Dundas and Lords Covington, Monboddo and Elliock. It is interesting that Monboddo dissented, as he was highly regarded by Burns and was befriended by him while he was in Edinburgh; perhaps a surprising choice for a man of alleged humanity. In addition, Burns's publisher William Creech was a committee member of the Edinburgh Committee for the Abolition of the Slave Trade; again, one would have thought Burns would have been an active supporter of the cause.

Burns's political views had previously been publicly attacked. In 1793 a number of Tories in the Dumfries district had formed themselves into a club for 'Supporting the Laws and Constitution of the Country' called the Loyal Natives Club. One of their number had composed a rhyme[5] critical of Burns and his liberal friends:

> Ye sons of Sedition, give ear to my song:
> Let Syme, Burns and Maxwell persuade every throng,
> With Craken, the attorney, and Mundell, the quack,
> Send Willie, the monger, to hell with a smack.

Burns had responded with the following reply entitled 'Ye True Loyal Natives':[6]

Ye true 'Loyal Natives', attend to my song:
In uproar and riot rejoice the night long!
From Envy and Hatred your corps is exempt,
But where is your shield from the darts of Contempt?

By the beginning of 1795, colours had to be pinned to the mast. Great Britain was making preparations for the expected invasion by France. The French forces had subdued Spain, Prussia, Holland and Austria, and part-time volunteer forces were formed to defend vulnerable landing areas such as Dumfries.

The Loyal Natives were quick to join the Royal Dumfries Volunteers, but some of the alleged republicans named by them also enlisted. The founder members included John Syme, Doctor James Mundell, William McCraken and Burns himself. Only Doctor William Maxwell ignored the call to arms, but that was hardly surprising. He is from a Jacobite family in the Stewartry of Kirkcudbright, was educated at a Jesuit college in France, and qualified as a doctor in Edinburgh. He was prominent in promoting the French revolutionary cause in Great Britain until war broke out in 1793, when he was constrained by worries about treasonable behaviour. So Burns and his liberal cronies drilled and practised combat without the good Doctor Maxwell. Burns composed a rousing song for the Volunteers entitled 'Does Haughty Gaul Invasion Threat?':[7]

Does haughty Gaul invasion threat?
Then let the loons beware, Sir!
There's Wooden Walls upon our seas
And volunteers on shore, Sir!
The Nith shall run to Corsincon,
And Criffel sink in Solway,
Ere we permit a foreign foe
On British ground to rally!

O, let us not, like snarling curs,
In wrangling be divided,
Till, slap! come in an unco loon,
And wi' a rung decide it!
Be Britain still to Britain true,
Among ourselves united!
For never but by British hands
Maun British wrangs be righted!

The kettle o' the Kirk and State,
Perhaps a clout may fail in't;
But deil a foreign tinkler loon
Shall ever ca a nail in't!
Our Fathers' Blude the kettle bought,
And wha wad dare to spoil it?
By Heav'ns! the sacrilegious dog
Shall fuel be to boil it!

The wretch that would a Tyrant own,
And the wretch, his true-born brother,
Who would set the Mob above the Throne,
May they be damn'd together!
Who will not sing "God Save the King"
Shall hang as high's the steeple;
But while we sing "God Save the King"
We'll ne'er forget The People!

I wonder if the words came easily to the republican element in the Volunteers!

Other notable friends of Burns who joined the Volunteers included the lawyers Samuel Clark and William Thomson of Moat; his landlord, John Hamilton; the landlord of the Globe tavern, William Hyslop; John McMurdo of Drumlanrig; Thomas Boyd, the builder; and Alexander Findlater from the Excise. Thomson later acted as factor *loco tutoris*, a sort of financial guardian to Burns's children after his death.

There was a by-election for the Stewartry of Kirkcudbright in the spring of 1795 following the death of Alexander Stewart, the sitting Member of Parliament. The small constituency, adjacent to Dumfries, had been the subject of a power-sharing arrangement among Stewart, Peter Johnston and James Murray of Broughton and Cally, but that had broken down when Murray eloped with Johnston's sister.

I acted as law agent for the Tory candidate Thomas Gordon of Balmaghie. Burns supported the Whig candidate, who, by an extraordinary coincidence, was Patrick Heron, one of the founders of the failed Douglas Heron Bank which had figured so large in the dispute Burns's father had had with his landlord at Lochlie fourteen years earlier. But as John Syme later told me after Burns's death, his enthusiasm for Heron was at least partly actuated by a suggestion by Heron that he might be able to assist in advancing Burns's career in the Excise.

Heron had the support of Henry Dundas, and the election campaign was keenly fought. Throughout the campaign I was treated with civility and cordiality by Patrick Heron and his law agent. I was also exempted – perhaps because of my previous friendship with William Nicol – from the abuse hurled at the Tory campaign by Burns, who composed slogans and ballads for Heron and against Gordon. I have to concede that these assails may well have contributed to the Whig's success.

In his 'Ballad Second: The Election',[8] he mentions three lawyers. Firstly John Bushby, friend of John Syme:

An' there'll be black-nebbit Johnie,
The tongue o' the trump to them a';
Gin he get na Hell for his haddin,
The Deil gets nae justice ava!

This is followed by a disrespectful mention of Maitland Bushby, John's son, who was admitted to the Faculty of Advocates in 1788 and had recently been appointed Sheriff of Wigtonshire:

An' there'll be Wigton's new sheriff—
Dame Justice fu' brawly has sped:
She's gotten the heart of a Bushby,
But Lord! what's become o' the head?

Not even Syme himself was exempted:

An' there'll be Stamp-office Johnie
Tak tent how ye purchase a dram!

'Ballad Third: John Bushby's Lamentation'[9] had the most serious consequences for Burns. Doctor James Muirhead, parish minister of Urr, was slighted as follows:

And by our banners march'd Muirhead,
And Buittle was na slack,
Whase haly priesthood nane could stain,
For wha could dye the black?

That proved to be a step too far. Muirhead was not slow in retaliating: he quoted and provided an adaptation of one of Martial's epigrams.[10]

Et delator es et calumniator,
Et fraudator es et negotiator,
Et fellator es et lanista: miror
Quare non habeas, Vacerra, nummos.

The translation of *fellator* was kind to Burns:

Vacerra, shabby son of whore
Why do thy patrons keep thee poor?
Bribe-worthy service, thou cans't boast
At once their bulwark and their host.

Thou art a sychophant, a traitor,
A liar, a calumniator,
Who conscience – hadst thou that – would'st sell,
Nay, lave the common sewer of Hell

For whisky – eke, most precious imp,
Thou art a rhymster, gauger, pimp;
Whence comes it then, Vacerra that
Thou still art poor as a church rat?

I understand his friends had never seen Burns so discomfited than when this was circulated in Dumfries and Edinburgh. He was aware that his educated friends would know that "fellator" does not translate as gauger, but as someone who indulges in perverted sexual practices. I actually remonstrated with Muirhead about his adaptation, and his disingenuous explanation was that Burns as an exciseman sucked from the cask.

John Syme and I had a professional relationship in that we were both involved in the factoring and management of landed estates in the south-west of Scotland. He often invited me to parties at Ryedale, but if I knew Burns was to be there I tended to decline the invitations as I felt Burns adopted a patronising attitude towards me, caused by a kind of inverted snobbery.

In June Burns and his friends were involved at the periphery of an unsavoury incident in Dumfries. The Strathspey Fencibles were quartered in the town, and were instructed to arrest some Irish tinkers who were in a nearby property. In the course of carrying out their mandate, they were fired upon by the tinkers, as a result of which one of the Fencibles was killed. The leader of the tinkers, one John O'Neill, was sent to Edinburgh for trial. Burns, being a liberal sort, thought it right that the man should have a fair defence, and prevailed upon the aforementioned Maria Riddell to journey to Edinburgh to persuade his old friend Harry Erskine to act as O'Neill's Advocate. Erskine agreed to act, but just as with William Brodie, Erskine failed to save his client from being condemned to death. The formidable Mrs Riddell would not be denied, however, and she appealed to Charles Fox, the leader of the Whigs in Parliament, and through him obtained a commutation of O'Neill's sentence.

I must say that after the election in 1795 Burns's health deteriorated rapidly, and when I last saw him he looked miserably ill. I know he was being hounded by creditors around this time, and in fact I suggested to Syme on one occasion that I might settle one of Burns's debts to a local shopkeeper. Syme advised me against it, citing Burns's pride.

Family tragedy struck him during his illness. In September his three-year-old daughter Elizabeth Riddell Burns died unexpectedly while she was in Mauchline. Burns was so unwell at the time that he was unable to travel to Ayrshire for the funeral.

His health did rally in the last quarter of the year, and it would seem that his relationship with Maria Riddell resumed. By this time, she had moved to Hallheaths near Lochmaben. I know very little about what passed between them at that time, but her memoirs indicate that the rift between them following the incident at Friar's Carse was healed.

Later

I was reinforced in my view about Burns's attitude to slavery when I learned that his patron, Patrick Heron, voted against abolition of the slave trade in 1796. The latent ambiguity in Burns's politics is also revealed by Heron being supported by Dundas, whom Burns allegedly loathed. Dundas said of Heron just before the latter's death that there was not a more respectable gentleman or friend of the Government in the House of Commons.

The poem 'A Man's a Man' was published in the Whig newspaper the *London Oracle* on 2nd June 1796 with Burns named as the author. This was only a few weeks before his death, and I have no doubt that, had he survived, he would have been convicted of sedition and ordered to be transported to Botany Bay.

I had little to do with Burns's family after his death although I was aware of the various appeals for support of his family, and of the various court proceedings in Edinburgh on the subject of copyright.

CHAPTER 18

DEMISE

1796

WILLIAM McCRAKEN

William McCraken was a lawyer in Dumfries, a friend of John Syme and a liberal thinker. He was one of the locals mentioned in the rhyme, composed in 1793 by the Loyal Natives Club, critical of Burns and his cronies, in which he is referred to as 'Craken the attorney'.

He joined the Royal Dumfries Volunteers with Burns in 1795.

He died in 1818 and is buried in St Michael's Churchyard, Dumfries.

My name is William McCraken. I am a lawyer. I am fifty-six years of age. I make this statement on 31st March 1812. At the beginning of the year 1796, conditions in the county of Dumfries were bad. Food supplies were running low due to a poor harvest and shortages caused by wartime conditions. There was, in fact, a riot in the town of Dumfries in March, after which supplies of food were made available.

Although Robert and I were Whigs, we had joined the Royal Dumfries Volunteers along with our Tory opponents, as we all felt that our country was under threat from a regime which had started out with great ideals but had degenerated into intolerance and repression. We were not, however, happy with some of the steps which our own government had taken such as curtailing free speech, which were in some ways equally reprehensible.

We were appalled at the verdicts reached by the Scottish courts and the sentences handed down in the sedition and treason trials of 1793 and 1794, and in November 1795, the government had introduced a measure, the Seditious Meetings Act, whose purpose was to restrict the size of public meetings to fifty persons, and to avoid the fomenting of discontent by requiring a license for lecturing and debating halls. This prompted much opposition, one outspoken objector in Edinburgh being Robert's friend and brother Freemason Harry Erskine, Dean of the Faculty of Advocates, who spoke at a meeting of objectors and moved the motions passed at that meeting.

That the Dean should take this stance outraged many members of Faculty, and eight advocates wrote to Erskine to advise that his re-election as Dean would be opposed. Such a move was unprecedented. The eight signatories were eminent – four of them are now judges (Lords Meadowbank, Craigie, Granton and Boyle).

They nominated Henry Dundas's nephew Robert Dundas, the Lord Advocate and a High Tory, as Dean.

Robert disliked Robert Dundas intensely. This was partly due to a slight Robert felt he had received from him about eight years previously when Robert had been invited to compose elegiac verses on the death of Dundas's father, Lord President Dundas. Robert had sent his composition to the Lord President's son, with a covering letter, but, as he put it, Dundas took no notice of the letter, the poem or the poet. Given that this incident occurred when Robert was in the heyday of his fame, his exasperation was understandable. This antipathy towards Dundas had greatly developed in the previous three years as Robert Dundas had appeared for the Crown in the great prosecutions for sedition and treason.

In the event, Harry Erskine's widespread popularity as a skilful and sympathetic lawyer was not sufficient to counter the Tory majority of members of Faculty and in January 1796, he was defeated by 123 votes to 38. An outraged Robert composed a new ballad, 'The Dean of the Faculty':[1]

> Dire was the hate at Old Harlaw
> That Scot to Scot did carry;
> And dire the discord Langside saw
> For beauteous, hapless Mary.
> But Scot with Scot ne'er met so hot
> Or were more in fury seen, Sir,
> Than 'twixt Hal and Bob for the famous job,
> Who should be the Faculty's Dean, Sir.
>
> This Hal for genius, wit, and lore
> Among the first was number'd;
> But pious Bob, 'mid learning's store
> Commandment the Tenth remember'd.

Yet simple Bob the victory got
And won his heart's desire:
Which shows that Heaven can boil the pot,
Tho' the Deil piss in the fire.

Squire Hal, besides, had in this case
Pretensions rather brassy,
For talents, to deserve a place
Are qualifications saucy;
So, their worships of the Faculty,
Quite sick of Merit's rudeness,
Chose one who should owe it all (d'ye see?)
To their gratis grace and goodness!

As once on Pisgah purg'd was the sight
Of a son of Circumcision,
So, may be, on this Pisgah height
Bob's purblind, mental vision.
Nay, Bobby's mouth may be open'd yet,
Till for eloquence you hail him,
And swear he has the Angel met
That met the Ass of Balaam.

In your heretic sins may ye live and die,
Ye heretic Eight and Thirty!
But accept, ye sublime majority,
My congratulations hearty!
With your honours, as with a certain King,
In your servants this is striking,
The more incapacity they bring
The more they're to your liking!

The last verse is particularly dangerous, and the poem was not widely circulated for fear of retribution. To their shame, in my opinion,

George Jos. Bell and Walter Scott were among those who voted for Dundas.

One of Robert's heroes had been Thomas Muir, the republican activist who was expelled from the Faculty of Advocates in 1793 when Erskine was Dean, and who was later convicted of seditious practices and sentenced to transportation to Botany Bay for fourteen years. On receiving the news of Erskine's humiliation, the Reverend George Hamilton, minister at Gladsmuir, a staunch Tory who had crossed literary swords with Robert some years previously, composed what he described as a consolatory epistle, 'The Telegraph',[2] purportedly from Muir, exiled in Botany Bay, to the former Dean. The introductory verses betray more gleeful revenge than consolation:

> From this remote, this melancholy shore;
> Round whose bleak rocks incessant tempests roar;
> Where sullen Convicts drag the clanking chain,
> And desolation covers all the plain;
> My heart, dear Dean, with anguish turns to you,
> And mourns the scenes, just opening in your view.
> Eager the Telegraphic board I rear,
> To paint the sorrows which you cannot hear.
> To pour the anguish of my heart, and tell,
> How late you flourished, –and how low you fell!–
>
> With grief I see, thy ancient honours past,
> Disgrace and shame o'ertake thee at the last.
> I see our Bretheren, deaf to freedom's voice,
> Desert the Dean, the object of their choice,
> Who, at the head, for ten long years had stood,
> Receiving double fees, – all for his country's good.

I see thee on this auspicious day,
Whilst ragged Patriots hail thee on thy way;
And Cinder-wenches, softening at the scene,
Sigh for the fate of the unhappy Dean.
I see thee slowly to the Court repair,
Thy pallid visage marked with deadly care,
Thy steps supported by the kind Adair;
Whilst Patriot Hay, a Brother's sorrow feels,
And Clerk, like Justice, hobbles at thy heels.

Tho' Wit and Genius both exert their power,
Vain all their efforts, this ill-omen'd hour;
The Puns which us'd in happier days of yore,
To set the willing circle in a roar,
The happy repartee, the bons mots fail,
And not a laugh attends the well told tale;
Not, tho' you every nerve of fancy strain,–
And gnaw your bitten nails with secret pain.

In vain the struggle; tho' the distant North,
And patriot West, pour all their heroes forth;
No human means can guard the envied place,
Nor save the sinking Dean from dire disgrace.

The vote is passed, and black balls fill the urn,
The silken gown is from thy shoulders torn,
And all thy titles, all thine honours pass
To deck the person of abhorred Dundas!

Although Robert's health was was poor, he was able to attend Masonic Lodge meetings with me. But at this time he was disconsolate, feeling that he had been abandoned by his Ayrshire and Edinburgh friends. In particular, he was upset that Mrs Frances Dunlop was ignoring his letters. After Robert's death I learned that she had been appalled by Robert's insensitivity towards how her family had been affected by the upheaval following the revolution in France.

Robert's attendance to Excise matters became intermittent and his income more or less dried up. In receiving no income, Robert was being treated the same as other excisemen, since those employees who had received a substantial increase in salary in the previous few years, so benefitted on the understanding that the increase was not payable in periods of absence. In fact, from the beginning of 1796 up to his death, he initially received full pay, then half pay, reducing eventually to nothing. I know he appealed for additional remuneration, and though his friend Robert Graham of Fintry, the Commissioner of Excise, was unable to sanction that, Graham very generously sent him £5 as a gift.

Robert asked me to help with a letter he had received from George Thomson about a problem he had encountered in relation to his first edition of *Select Scottish Airs*, published in 1793. Apparently a music seller in Edinburgh had imported from Dublin and sold some copies of a pirated edition. Robert and I agreed the wording of a certificate[3] he would send to George, in the following terms:

> I do hereby certify, that all the Songs of my writing, published, and to be published, by Mr George Thomson of Edinburgh, are so published by my Authority. And, moreover, that I never empowered any other person to publish any of the Songs written by me for his Work. And I authorize him to prosecute any person or persons, who shall publish or vend ANY of those Songs without his consent. In testimony whereof &c.

> ROBERT BURNS

George later told me that he had raised an action against the music seller based on Robert's certificate, but in exchange for an apology and making a donation to charity (and meeting his expenses), George had decided to proceed no further against him.

Another general election was called in May and once again Robert lent support to Patrick Heron by composing a new satirical ballad containing a measure of vitriol towards the supporters of Heron's opponent, the Honourable Montgomery Granville John Stewart, sixth son of the Earl of Galloway. He took the opportunity in 'Heron Election: Ballad Fourth'[4] to include a verse responding to the lampoon he had suffered from the pen of Doctor James Muirhead, parish minister at Urr, in the previous general election campaign, which had hurt him so much:

> Here's armorial bearings
> Frae the manse of Urr
> The crest, an auld crab-apple
> Rotten to the core.

Thanks in part to Robert's efforts, once again Heron was elected.

At the beginning of July, Robert was advised by his doctors to take the waters at a nearby village called Brow where there was a chalybeate spring, and to bathe in the Solway. While he was there, on 5th July, he had dinner with his intimate friend Mrs Maria Riddell, who was renting a property in the area following the collapse of her husband Walter's fortunes and their removal from Woodley Park. Mrs Riddell has subsequently written that the stamp of death was already on Robert's features. She herself was unwell at the time, and told Burns that she hoped he would live to write her epitaph. She never saw Robert again.

I never understood why our mutual friend William Maxwell, Robert's physician, thought taking the waters of the Solway, even in the month of July, was a suitable course of treatment for a man in Robert's frail condition. Robert himself had a secret fear that the business of bathing in salt water was dangerous and might prove to be fatal to him. I visited him at Brow on 15th July and saw him again a few days later, when he had returned to Dumfries. I was horrified at his deteriorated condition, and Maxwell told me that the end was near.

John Syme and I had frequent discussions about the Burns family and we decided that he should write to Alexander Cunningham in Edinburgh asking him to consider what might be done for them. Cunningham suggested that there might firstly be a subscription for Mrs Burns and the family.

By now, Robert was extremely unwell and agitated, as he was being sued by a haberdasher to whom he owed an account and he was fearful of being imprisoned for debt. I helped him write to his cousin James Burness and to George Thomson, his publisher in Edinburgh, asking them to help, and to his brother Gilbert warning him that the debt he owed Robert would need to be repaid to support the family if Robert died.

Robert died on Thursday 21st July, and the funeral took place on the following Monday. Syme was largely responsible for organising it. An impressive gathering of town and country folk lined the streets to watch the assembly. I was one of the twenty Royal Dumfries Volunteers at the head of the procession, all wearing black armbands. Behind us was the military band belonging to the Cinque Ports Cavalry, then the coffin carried by six of the Volunteers, then Robert's brother Gilbert with some local notables, then the rest of the Volunteers and lastly a guard of the Angusshire Fencibles. There was a bit of a cacophony of sounds, with the band playing the 'Dead March in Saul' and the bells of all the Dumfries churches tolling at intervals. At the churchyard, a firing party from the Volunteers fired three volleys over the coffin as it was lowered into the ground. Mrs Burns had, of course, been unable to attend, as she had gone into labour on the very morning of the funeral. Robert's son, named Maxwell, was born later that day. There was a concern that the infant seemed to be a weakling, lacking energy, and in fact he died young.

Cunningham was keen that Syme become what would in effect be a trustee along with Patrick Miller, Robert's former landlord at Ellisland, to receive and disburse whatever funds were collected for the benefit of Mrs Burns and the children, and that he agree to act along with him in collecting from Robert's friends and acquaintances any poems and letters in their possession with a view to publishing a posthumous volume for the benefit of Mrs Burns and the family. Syme was happy to take on these responsibilities, but was keen to widen the range of persons to whom friends could return Robert's unpublished works. Patrick Miller was hesitant about becoming involved, and, to my mind somewhat surprisingly, was rather parsimonious in his donation to the fund. However, he did agree to act on the Committee formed in Dumfries along with his son, among others.

We had an initial concern about William Creech, Robert's Edinburgh publisher, as Robert had continually complained that he had been duped into selling him his copyright for a pittance, and the plans for a posthumous edition would be seriously undermined if we did not get his co-operation. Several of Robert's friends agreed to write to Creech encouraging him to assist us in every way, but there was a general feeling that we might encounter a degree of hesitation on his part, and indeed Cunningham wrote to Syme on 30th July confirming that Creech had affirmed that he would not part with the copyright.

At the beginning of August we went through Robert's papers.

We could find no Will. Our main task was to separate the small amount of wheat from the chaff. Among the wheat we located letters to Robert from Mrs Agnes McLehose, and we immediately recognised that these could cause at least embarrassment. Cunningham advised me that he was being pressed by Robert Ainslie, the Edinburgh lawyer, a former friend of Robert's who now appeared to be acting for Mrs McLehose, to arrange to return to her the letters she had written to Robert, which we agreed to do. Doctor Maxwell and John McMurdo, Robert's close friend who was chamberlain to the Duke of Queensberry at Drumlanrig, agreed to go through the remaining papers and index them before transmission to Doctor James Currie in Liverpool, as he had been prevailed upon to write Robert's biography. Currie had been a college friend of John Syme, and had met Robert only once at a brief interview in 1792. I believe that Syme himself, as well as Maria Riddell and Professor Dugald Stewart, previously declined the offer to be the biographer.

Maxwell and McMurdo made little progress in the ensuing months of 1796, and at the end of the year sent everything to Currie in Liverpool. In his acknowledgement he described what was before him as a "huge and shapeless mass". I must say I felt a bit guilty about our failure in Dumfries to weed out more of what turned out to be irrelevant material.

As mentioned previously, Robert had never got round to making a Will: I advised Mrs Burns to consult William Wallace, a local lawyer, about Robert's estate, and on 16th September the Commissary Court in Dumfries appointed Mrs Burns his executrix in her capacity as widow (or 'relict', as it is formally described), and it was found that his estate comprised debts due to Robert (described as 'the defunct') as detailed:[5]

Item the principal Sum of Five Pounds sterling contained in a Promissory Note dated the Fourteenth day of July last granted by Sir William Forbes & Company, Bankers in Edinburgh, to George Thomson, payable on demand, which Note is by the said George Thomson indorsed payable to the defunct.

Item the principal Sum of Ten Pounds sterling contained in a draft dated the Fifteenth day of July last drawn by Robert Christie upon the Manager for the British Linen Company in Edinburgh in favour of James Burness or order, which draft is by the said James Burness indorsed payable to the defunct.

So it seemed that Robert's music publisher and his cousin had each responded positively to his last request, though he had not survived to use the funds. It was surprising that the debt owed to Robert by his brother Gilbert was not included in this document.

Mrs Burns was therefore left without capital resources of any note. Robert had been contributing to the Excise Pension Fund for Widows and Orphans during his service and, following his death, Mrs Burns was entitled to an annual pension of £10.

Some friends and acquaintances initially rallied round, but the year ended with the Burns family in difficult circumstances. The initial response to the appeals for support had yielded very little. That was partly due, I think, to Robert's largely undeserved reputation as a heavy drinker in the last few years of his life. But all that was about to change thanks to the efforts of a small number of Robert's friends and the determination of one man: Doctor James Currie, born in Dumfriesshire and then living and working in Liverpool, a man who hardly knew Robert, would prove to be the financial saviour of the

Burns family by compiling and editing a new edition of Burns's work.

Later

The sums the Burns family received for the sale of Currie's publication greatly contributed to their financial wellbeing, but his commentary on the latter years of Robert's life painted the poet in a bad light, from which he has acquired an undeserved reputation.

CHAPTER 19

FAMILY SUPPORT

1796–1809

WILLIAM THOMSON OF MOAT

William Thomson of Moat had a successful legal practice in Dumfries. He got to know Robert Burns well after they enlisted as Royal Dumfries Volunteers in 1795 along with their mutual friends John Syme, John McMurdo and William McCraken. Thomson was part of the firing party at Burns's funeral. He became Provost of Dumfries in 1819 and was re-elected twice.

He was appointed by the Court of Session in 1798 to look after the financial interests of Burns's surviving legitimate children Robert Junior (then eleven), Francis-Wallace (then eight), William-Nicol (then six), James (then three) and Maxwell (then one year old). He was to hold the funds collected for the children until each was fourteen, when the share would be transferred to their mother for their benefit. Unfortunately neither Francis-Wallace (died 1803) nor Maxwell (died 1799) survived to attain fourteen, so Thomson's duties as factor lasted until James reached that age in 1808.

The saga of the settlement by Gilbert Burns of his debt to his brother ran well beyond the end of Thomson's formal role, but Thomson continued to act on behalf of Mrs Jean Burns, and was involved in agreeing the final financial settlement with Gilbert in 1820.

M y name is William Thomson. I am a lawyer. I am sixty-five years of age. I make this statement on 31st March 1835.

I was not initially involved in the arrangements for the Burns family. John Syme and the Edinburgh lawyer, Alexander Cunningham, headed up the efforts to raise funds, the former being much more successful than the latter. Edinburgh donations were less than £180, whereas Dumfries contributed over £500. The Committee which had been formed to collect and administer the donations included Syme, John McMurdo and Robert's physician, Doctor William Maxwell. They met at the beginning of December 1797 and recorded that they had resolved that, for the better direction of the affairs of the funds collected, it would be advisable to have a factor *loco tutoris* appointed, and that, although Robert's widow Jean had given the Committee authority to manage the donations and fix the extent of any provision to be made for her out of the funds with the balance being divided among the children, the members of the Committee were not minded to exercise those powers without proper authority from the court. What that meant was that an independent person appointed by the court would administer any funds the Committee released to the boys on their behalf.

They therefore recorded in a minute[1] that they were happy for Mrs Burns to present a Petition for my appointment as the factor, but for guidance resolved:

1. That the whole amount of the subscriptions and produce of their publications of the posthumous works of Mr Burns shall until the youngest of the children be past the years of pupilarity remain under one or more capitals, and the committee therefore agree that the factor to be appointed shall manage the same, reserving always to the committee full powers hereafter to fix

what provisions they may choose to allow therefrom to the widow, and also what sums they may judge fit to be appropriated for the education and putting into business any of the children, if it be found requisite to break into the capital for these purposes.

2. That in the meantime Mrs Burns and the children shall be supported out of the proceeds of the said capital reserving power to the committee to fix the extent of the annual sum for this purpose from time to time as the funds and circumstances of the family may allow and require.

3. Under these reservations and conditions the committee appoint the funds now realised and vouchers and other papers relative thereto to be delivered to the factor when appointed upon his Receipt granted on the back of these minutes–a copy to be delivered to him for his direction.

Such an appointment required to be made by the Court of Session in Edinburgh, and I arranged for my Edinburgh correspondent Andrew McWhinnie to instruct the presentation of the required Petition.

Counsel prepared the Petition[2] on behalf of Mrs Burns

UNTO THE RIGHT HONOURABLE
THE LORDS OF COUNCIL AND SESSION
Petition
of
Mrs Jean Armour,
otherwise BURNS, Widow of the
deceased Mr Robt Burns,
lately residing in Dumfries

HUMBLY SHEWETH

That the said Robert Burns died sometime ago, without having executed any Settlement or nomination of Tutors to Robert, Francis-Wallace, William-Nicol, and Maxwell Burns, the infant children of the marriage between him and the Petitioner.

That after the death of Mr Burns, several Gentlemen who respected his talents, and felt for the destitute situation of his family, set on foot a public subscription for their relief, and in consequence thereof the generosity of the public has supplied a fund which will afford an agential aid towards their maintenance and Education.

That as none of the Children have yet attained the age which would entitle them to choose Curators, the Petitioner, with the approbation of other friends and of several Gentlemen who have acted as a Committee for managing the Subscription for their behoof, makes the present application to your Lordships for having a factor *loco tutoris* appointed to them, and she begs leave humbly to suggest Mr William Thomson of Moat, Writer in Dumfries, as a proper person to be appointed to that office and who, at her request, and that of the Gentlemen of the Committee, has agreed to undertake the charge if your Lordships shall think it proper to appoint him.

> **MAY IT THEREFORE** please your Lordships to nominate and appoint the said William Thomson or any other person whom you shall think proper to be factor *loco tutoris* to the said Robert, Francis-Wallace, William-Nicol and Maxwell Burns, the Petitioner's infant children, with the usual powers, such factor always finding sufficient

caution, in terms of your Lordships'
Acts of Sederunt, before Extract.

ACCORDING TO JUSTICE, &c.

On 16th December 1797 I was appointed. A couple of weeks
later the omission of James Glencairn Burns in the Petition was
noticed, and I had to arrange for Jean to send a letter[3] to Mr
McWhinnie in the following terms:

Dumfries 26 Jany.1798

Sir

An unlucky omission happened in the former mandate
by me for having a factor *loco tutoris* appointed to my
children, the name of my son James (who is the
immediate older child to Maxwell) having been
overlooked. I authorise you therefore to apply for
having Mr Thomson appointed also to the above
office for behoof of the said child, for which shall be
a sufficient authority. I am Sir

Your mo: obs.
Jean Burns

This obviously necessitated immediate action and Mr McWhinnie
lodged a second Petition[4] in the following terms:

UNTO THE RIGHT HONOURABLE
THE LORDS OF COUNCIL AND SESSION
Petition
of
Mrs Jean Armour,
otherwise BURNS, Widow of the

deceased Mr Robt Burns,
lately residing in Dumfries

HUMBLY SHEWETH

That the Petitioner with the approbation of the other friends of her children, sometime ago made an application to your Lordships for having a factor *loco tutoris* appointed to Robert, Francis-Wallace, William-Nicol, and Maxwell Burns, infant children of the marriage between her and the said deceased Robert Burns; and she suggested Mr William Thomson of Moat, Writer in Dumfries, as a proper person to be appointed to that office. After the Petition had been intimated in the usual form, your Lordships were pleased, by Interlocutor of 16th December 1797 to nominate and appoint the said William Thomson to be factor *loco tutoris* to the said Robert, Francis-Wallace, William-Nicol and Maxwell Burns, the Petitioner's infant children, with the usual powers, he always finding caution before Extract, in terms of the Act of Sederunt.

That in the Letter or Mandate transmitted by the Petitioner to her Agent authorising the said application, she unfortunately omitted to insert the name of James Burns, the youngest but one of her infant Children, and of consequence his name was not mentioned in the Petition; and the omission was not discovered until after your Lordships' Interlocutor appointing the factor was pronounced which renders the present application necessary in order to supply the defect thereby occasioned before the factory shall be extracted.

MAY IT THEREFORE please your Lordships to nominate and appoint the said William Thomson to be factor *loco tutoris* also to the said James Burns, the youngest but one of Petitioner's infant children, with the usual powers, the said William Thomson always finding sufficient caution before Extract, in terms of the Act of Sederunt.

ACCORDING TO JUSTICE, &c.

On 10th February 1798 I became factor to all five children, and the Committee transferred the funds held to me.

I had to lodge in court a list of the assets to which the children were entitled at the date of my appointment. This was rather tricky, as some eighteen months had elapsed since Robert's death and various sums had been received by Mrs Burns as Robert's executrix. Apart from what was owed to Robert by his brother Gilbert on the Note, originally for £200, Robert's estate consisted of his furniture and effects, the balance of a small loan he had made to his friend, the schoolmaster James Clarke, and the sums of £5 and £10 gifted to him by his music publisher George Thomson and his cousin James Burness just before his death. Mrs Burns, of course, retained the furniture etc. and she had collected the small cash sums. As Robert left no Will, his widow's entitlement was to only one third of these assets, and the remainder should have passed to the children. As these assets had clearly been used to benefit the family, I simply recorded that these items had been applied in that way, and I did not seek to include them in the estate under my charge.

The debt by Gilbert was another matter entirely. I wrote to him on 23rd April 1798 seeking his proposals for settlement as the outstanding sum would have been of great benefit to the family. He replied in the following terms:[5]

> Sir,
>
> I received yours of the 23rd curt. I will either pay the bill due by me to my deceased brother or renew it with some caution as may be accepted, as soon as it is in my power, meantime as there were some accounts betwixt my brother and I unsettled at the time of my brother's death, and I have paid some funeral and other accounts since and advanced some money for the family. I intend to be in Dumfries towards the end of May or beginning of June in order to settle these and will then take such measures for settling the bill as may be agreeable.
>
> I am, Sir, your most
obedient servant,
>
> Mossgiel, 30th. April,1798   Gilbert Burns

'Caution' in the sense used by Gilbert would be a form of guarantee. When I met with Gilbert at the end of May he gave me a reconciliation of how he arrived at a figure of £164 as the balance owed by him to Robert under the original bill for £200. Interest at 5 per cent on the balance had been compounded giving a credit of £33, but apparently Robert had agreed to pay an annuity of £5 to his mother, and board and lodging and education costs for Bess Paton, his illegitimate daughter who was living with Gilbert and the family at Mossgiel. These deductions were about £18 and £26 respectively, and some minor charges for goods and services reduced the net sum at Robert's death to £183.

Some expenses had been incurred by Gilbert and accepted by Mrs Burns with one exception (which John Syme was able to verify), so a computation brought out about £158 due as at 17th September 1797.

Gilbert also gave the committee a statement of his own affairs when he met with them on 30th May. That showed that his realisable assets were less than his liabilities. The committee considered that he should make a payment of £50 in reduction of the debt to avoid the commencement of action against him for recovery. After the meeting Gilbert went to see John McMurdo to plead his case, as John had been unable to attend the meeting. John wrote to Doctor Maxwell explaining that, in his view, the best chance of recovery would be to allow Gilbert more time rather than push him into bankruptcy. Gilbert had convinced him that he could raise £40 by the end of July, and John exhorted the committee to agree to that part payment and the granting of a new bond. The committee was persuaded by John, and on 27th August 1798 I entered into an agreement with Gilbert in the following terms:[6]

> The foregoing State having been examined by the said Gilbert Burns in Mossgiel, and by William Thomson of Moat, writer in Dumfries, factor *loco tutoris* to the children of the deceased Robert Burns, late in Dumfries, they find the calculations to be just and that upon the supposition of the said Gilbert Burns being found entitled to an allowance of the sums brought to his credit in the foregoing State, the balance due by him on his bill for Two hundred Pounds to the said Robert Burns dated the Eighteenth day of December One thousand seven hundred and ninety-two years payable one day after date will in that case be only one hundred and fifty-eight pounds fifteen shillings and five pence

halfpenny bearing Interest from the Seventh day of September, MDCC and ninety seven years.

But in regard the said Gilbert Burns has vouchers for only a very few of the articles brought to his credit in the preceding, the said William Thomson does not consider himself, acting as factor *loco tutoris* for the pupils, entitled to allow credit for sums that are not legally vouched, however just he may suppose them to be, yet in the circumstances of the case he agrees to supercede payment of the contents of the said bill all but the above balance of one hundred and fifty-eight pounds fifteen shillings and five pence halfpenny with interest thereon from Seventh day of September last either until all the pupils shall arrive at the age of fourteen years when they will be entitled to judge and determine for themselves whether the unvouched articles shall be allowed or not, or until that point shall be determined by a Court of Law. It being understood and declared by both parties that nothing contained in this docquet shall hurt or prejudice the claims or objections of either party, so far as regards the articles brought to the Credit of the said Gilbert Burns in the preceding State. But that his claim for allowance thereof and all objections competent against the same are hereby secured and reserved entire to said Gilbert Burns and the said William Thomson and his pupils respectively, and that no prescription shall run against either party until a complete Settlement of the contents of said bill shall take place: In Witness Whereof this docquet written upon this and the preceding page by John Dickson, clerk to the said William Thomson, is subscribed by us at Dumfries this Twenty-seventh day of August One thousand seven hundred and ninety-eight years before these witnesses the said John Dickson, and Darand Glen,

Writer in Dumfries. It being hereby admitted by the said William Thomson that upon the Sixteenth day of July last he received Forty pounds Sterling from Mr Burns in part settlement of the aforesaid sum, the receipt of which was acknowledged by letter of Eighteenth July last.

Darand Glen, Witness	William Thomson
John Dickson, Witness	Gilbert Burns

This document was intended to establish where everyone stood, while preserving the right of Robert's children to question the deductions which Gilbert had made. The exclusion of prescription simply means that the children's right to challenge Gilbert's deductions would not be affected by lapse of time.

There were two principal sources of funds ingathered by me: those contributions which had been made initially by friends and admirers of Robert for the alleviation of the straitened circumstances of Mrs Burns and the children; and subsequently, the fees and subscriptions generated by the posthumous publications of Robert's works. My duty was to make appropriate payments for the maintenance of the children, under guidance from the Committee, and to account to each child for his share of the funds when he attained fourteen years of age.

Tragically, two of the boys died before they became entitled to their shares. Maxwell died in 1799 aged two and Francis-Wallace died in 1803 aged thirteen, so my duties as factor came to an end on 12th August 1808 when James Glencairn was fourteen.

My involvement with the Burns family was not, however, limited to the factory on behalf of the children. I have become a kind of factotum for the whole family. I had to negotiate and document the arrangements for Gilbert's debt, as previously detailed. I was also involved in chasing up the recovery of contributions from friends and admirers, in particular the sums collected in London by Sir James Shaw, then plain James Shaw, an Ayrshire lad who had made good as a merchant there. Shaw was a nephew of Gilbert Burns's wife Jean Breckenridge and later became Lord Mayor of London in 1805, and in that capacity led Lord Nelson's funeral procession in 1806. He was knighted in 1809. The Committee was aware, by reason of letters John Syme had received in 1798, that Shaw had collected substantial sums, but nothing had been sent to Dumfries. The Committee was so exercised by this failure that they instructed me to commence proceedings for recovery, but happily it transpired that there had been a misunderstanding. Shaw had sent the funds – £500 – to the magistrates of Ayr in the form of a security yielding 3 per cent. I received a letter dated 14th October 1800 from the Town Clerk of Ayr in the following terms:[7]

Dear Sir

Your Letter of the 9th current to the Magistrates of this Burgh came duly to hand, and I am desired by them to acquaint you that as far back as May 1799 the Magistrates were applied to by Mr James Shaw merchant in London to become Guardians to the widow and Children of the late Mr Burns, The Scots Poet, with respect to a subscription that Mr Shaw was then going forward with, which he expected to bring up to £500. The Magistrates agreed to the Request, and in May last they had a Letter from Mr Shaw covering a voucher for £500 Sterling bought into the Three per cent annuities in their name which is understood to be for behoof of Mr Burns's family.

The interest of this Stock is payable half yearly, and will be regularly remitted to you as the Magistrates draw it from London, and, as Mr Shaw in his Letter suggests, as the children come of age £100 of Stock can be sold and paid to such child to set him or her out in the world, taking always care that security be given for the widow's liferent thereof.

I am, Sir, Your
most obedient servant,
David Lomond
Town Clerk
Ayr

Ayr, 14th October 1800

By then, of course, Maxwell had died, so the £500 was due to be divided four ways. In the year 1800, Robert Junior received a one-quarter share of his entitlement (£125). Francis-Wallace died in 1803, a month before he would have attained fourteen, at which point a one-third share of his prospective entitlement was made over to Robert Junior (£41), leaving £334 to be divided between William-Nicol in 1806 and James in 1808. My role as factor ended on James's fourteenth birthday, but by then, as mentioned, I was acting as Mrs Jean Burns's lawyer, so I had a continuing involvement with the family.

Robert Junior was a constant source of unease for the Committee administering the Family Fund. In some ways this was ironic as he had received more financial support in his education than his brothers, thanks in part to a generous endowment by the late Captain Robert Riddell's brother Alexander. The Committee frequently required to settle debts incurred by him, and even his uncle Gilbert was unable to divert him from his spendthrift ways.

There were further calls for support from Robert Junior, and in 1821, when Gilbert finally repaid his debt to the Family Fund, £222 was sent to him to alleviate his financial situation. A few years later he was made bankrupt, and in March 1831 he obtained a Discharge which recorded that the son of the celebrated Scotch poet of that name, described as a clerk in the Stamp Office, had a salary of £200 a year, out of which he had to support a wife and daughter, as well as five other children. His debts amounted to £516, £200 of which were for Law costs. Robert was declared entitled to his Discharge, the Court ordering £70 a year out of his salary to be set aside for his creditors. In 1833 he returned to Dumfries, having retired with the benefit of a pension.

In sharp contrast to their elder brother, both William-Nicol and James Glencairn had successful careers in the East India Company, and neither required financial support after completion of their education and their setting up in employment.

Mrs Burns's income from the Family Fund was about £60 annually. Following her death on 26th March 1834, the Family Fund was wound up and distributed. The Trustees had made an *ex gratia* distribution of £200 to each of Robert's illegitimate daughters, Bess Paton and Elizabeth Park (known as Betty Burns), when they were twenty-one. As to the remainder Robert received his share, but William-Nicol gifted his share to his uncle Robert Armour in trust for his niece Sarah in 1833[8] and James also passed his share to Sarah in 1834.[9] Sarah is the only surviving child of James and his wife Sarah Robinson. Their two other children died young, and James's wife herself died while giving birth to Sarah in India. William-Nicol is married but has no children, and I infer that Sarah is his favourite niece, in view of the financial provision he has made for her. Robert Junior lives up to his father's reputation for producing children out of wedlock.

During his lifetime Burns was frequently in dread of being imprisoned, either for debt or following the issue of a writ *in meditatione fugae* from a girl he had caused to become pregnant. In his last months he became morbidly fearful of this, but he never actually suffered the indignity of being gaoled. Sadly, his best friend from his latter years, Doctor William Maxwell, the former revolutionary, was committed to prison for debt in 1820, and I was one of his creditors! He owed me personally over £250.

Maxwell had unwisely purchased Netherwood Estate, near Dumfries, and hopelessly overextended himself in the purchase of the property. He had ambitious plans to convert the estate into a dairy farm, and opened a shop in Dumfries for the sale of its produce by retail. He incurred great expense in erecting buildings, purchasing stock, and improving, enclosing and otherwise adapting the property for carrying on the operations of a dairy upon an extended scale. This was all horribly reminiscent of Burns's farming history, though Burns, of course, never had sufficient capital to buy property.

Maxwell's financial problems were compounded by what he described as a tedious and expensive law suit with the seller of Netherwood, and, the returns from the dairy not having matched his expectations, he was reduced to bankruptcy.

In 1815 he petitioned for his own sequestration, and I was appointed interim factor. At my request, Robert Threshie, a lawyer in Dumfries, was appointed permanent trustee in bankruptcy. Matters moved slowly, and on 7th January 1820, another frustrated creditor, William Young, cashier of the Galloway Bank at Castle Douglas, arranged for Maxwell to be incarcerated in the Tolbooth in Dumfries in virtue of letters of caption[10] procured from the Bill Chamber. These letters required John Kerr, one of the baillies of Dumfries:

> to put, keep hold and detain the person of Doctor William Maxwell, late of Netherwood, presently Physician in Dumfries in sure ward, firmance, and captivity, within your tolbooth or other of your

warding places therein to remain upon his own proper
charges and expenses, aye and until he make payment
to the also therein designed William Young of the sum
of money principal and interest contained and due.

Maxwell was duly thrown into prison, but his friends rallied round
and his own doctor procured his release from the Tolbooth in
Dumfries on the grounds of his illness, subject to supervised
detention in his house. Following this, his sequestration was promptly
concluded. The deficiency in assets was over £7,400, according to
the trustee's report. On 1st March 1820, following the granting by
him of a Disposition *cessio bonorum*, he was set free and discharged
from his creditors putting any diligence in execution upon him.
Thankfully, Doctor Maxwell was also relieved of the obligation to
wear a dyvour's habit. By Act of Sederunt of 18th July 1688, the
Court of Session had ordained that unless so relieved, every
bankrupt, after release from prison and in all time coming, was
required to wear "a bonnet, partly of a brown, and partly of a yellow
colour, with uppermost hose, or stockings, on his legs, half brown
and half yellow colloured".[11] One can easily appreciate why Burns
had been so exercised about imprisonment for debt, for both his
father William and himself!

CHAPTER 20

COPYRIGHT

FROM 1800

PROFESSOR GEORGE JOSEPH BELL

George Joseph Bell was born in Edinburgh on 26th March 1770. He was admitted to the Faculty of Advocates in 1791. He was both a practical and academic lawyer.

In 1822, Bell was unanimously elected by the Faculty of Advocates as Professor of Scots Law in the University of Edinburgh, the motion being seconded by Sir Walter Scott.

Bell's most famous work is his *Principles of the Law of Scotland* (1829) which became a standard authority and is still cited and followed in many cases to this day.

He died in 1843.

My name is George Joseph Bell. I am an advocate and also Professor of Scots Law in the University of Edinburgh. I am sixty-five years of age. I make this statement on 31st December 1835.

I deal in this statement with a number of confidential matters about Robert Burns's alleged inamorata Clarinda, whose real identity – Mrs Agnes McLehose – is still not widely known. I have passed this statement (the only copy) to her son, Andrew, with instructions that it be not published until after his mother's death.

I was, of course, aware of the effect Robert Burns had on the literati of Edinburgh during his times in the city, but I never met him myself. My contemporary and fellow advocate the late Sir Walter Scott, latterly an accomplished and widely praised writer of prose, who became a member of the Faculty of Advocates just under a year after my admission, did meet Burns and always held his literary ability, if not his politics, in high regard.

My involvement was in two cases on copyright issues which greatly affected Burns's family. My understanding of the history of the copyright in Burns's works, according to information supplied to me, is as follows.

The first edition of his poems was published in Kilmarnock in 1786. The next year, Burns sold a second edition, published in Edinburgh, to William Creech, the Edinburgh publisher for whom also I was later to act. In 1793 a further edition was published by Mr Creech, Burns adding twenty new poems to the collection. Copyright in the 1793 Edinburgh Edition was also vested in Mr Creech by virtue of the agreement Burns had entered into on 22nd October 1787 on advice from Henry Mackenzie. According to the Statute of Anne, copyright in the additional twenty poems would not expire until 1807. Mr Creech then entered into a contract with the London publishers

Cadell and Davies to the effect of vesting the copyright held by him in them jointly.

In 1796 Burns died. His family was impoverished, and the only potential source of income for them, to supplement the very modest pension Mrs Burns was awarded by the Excise, was from the further publication of his works. A Committee of Trustees was formed to support the family, and Doctor James Currie of Liverpool, an admirer of Burns, kindly agreed to be the editor of a complete collection of Burns's works. After protracted negotiations, on 25th February 1800 Messers Creech, Cadell and Davies entered into an agreement with Doctor William Maxwell, John McMurdo and John Syme, Trustees for the family; Gilbert Burns, brother of the deceased (as nearest male heir to his surviving legitimate children); Mrs Jean Armour or Burns, widow of the deceased and mother of the surviving legitimate children; and William Thomson of Moat (the children's factor *loco tutoris*). The agreement proceeded on the narrative that Cadell and Davies and Mr Creech (all of whom I was acting for) were entitled to the copyright in the works of the deceased already published, for the remainder of a period of years then unexpired; that the family was in possession of several original works and writings the deceased himself had composed, but which were then unpublished; and that Trustees and the family had agreed with my clients that some of these unpublished works, as selected by Doctor Currie and with the advice and consent of the trustees, should be incorporated into a new edition, to be published in four volumes *octavo*, with a life of the deceased written by Currie prefixed. Therefore, subject to certain stipulations and obligations to be performed by my clients, the Trustees and the family did:

> give, grant, bargain, sell, assign, and confirm unto
> Thomas Cadell, William Davies and William Creech,
> their executors, administrators, and assigns, all that the

said intended edition, not exceeding 2000 copies, in four volumes octavo of the Works of the said Robert Burns, with his life, by the said James Currie, to be prefixed thereto, so to be printed and published, under the superintendence of the said James Currie, and at the costs, charges, and expenses of the said Thomas Cadell and William Davies; and also, all the copyright, right of authorship, use, interest, trust, property, claim, demand, privilege, and authority whatsoever which the said Robert Burns in his lifetime had, or which they, the said William Maxwell, John McMurdo, John Syme, Gilbert Burns, Jean Armour, and William Thomson, or any or either of them, or any other person or persons, now have, or of right ought to have, by force or virtue of any law, statute, usage, or custom whatsoever, or howsoever, of, in, and to the said Works of the said Robert Burns, and his life to be prefixed thereto, and to be contained in such intended edition, and every part and parts thereof. And also of, in and to all other works and compositions of the said Robert Burns, which may not be inserted in such intended edition, together with full power and authority to print and reprint all such works, and to sell, vend and dispose of the same from time to time and at all times hereafter. To have and to hold the said intended edition, and all future editions of the said works, and also the copyright in and to all the works of the said Robert Burns and all other premises with the appurtenances hereby assigned; and all profit, benefit, and advantage, that shall or may arise by and from printing, reprinting, publishing, vending, and disposing of the same, unto the said Thomas Cadell and William Davies, their executors, administrators, or assigns, as their own proper goods and chattels, and sole and exclusive property for ever, for so long time as such property can or may by law subsist, remain, and endure.[1]

The effect of this document and the previous assignment by the deceased to Mr Creech in 1787 was to transfer outright to Messrs Cadell, Davies and Creech all rights of property or, in other words, exclusive privilege in these works which had been held by the persons of the deceased or his representatives.

Currie's edition raised £1,400 for the benefit of Burns's family.

In 1802, T. Stewart & A. Macgoun, Booksellers in Glasgow, published an edition of Burns's poems to which was added an appendix consisting of Burns's correspondence with someone named as 'Clarinda', in which Burns himself was referred to as 'Sylvander'. This book included original letters from Burns to a Mrs Agnes McLehose, who was a married woman at the time of her relationship with Burns. She is a cousin of the late William Craig, who became a Court of Session judge as Lord Craig in 1792.

I advised my clients to seek an interdict restraining the publication and, pending a full hearing, they were granted an interim interdict on 18th November 1802.

The case was put out for report, and I prepared our written submissions. I thought it would add weight to our case if Gilbert Burns (as brother of the deceased), Jean Armour or Burns (as widow), and William Thomson of Moat (factor *loco tutoris* to the children) were joined in the action, so on 15th February 1803, they, along with the Trustees for the Burns family, were sisted into the case. I produced what I thought was a compelling series of arguments, albeit including somewhat flowery language, to describe the circumstances in which the letters came to be written. I described Burns[2] as one of those men who are "constantly the victims of some fair enslaver", and conceded that Burns had been unable to resist the force of Clarinda's charms. Burns had "poured forth to this goddess of his idolatry the expressions of his ardent and passionate adoration".

Counsel for Stewart & Macgoun – Archibald Fletcher – argued

that ownership of the physical letters had passed to Clarinda, and as she had acquired them without any condition or limitation, she was entitled to every legal use she could make of them. In addition, there would be no breach of confidence involved, since whoever makes any communication to another, relies on that person's discretion, and can never hope to prevent the communication being passed on.

I countered that the case turned on whether the addressee of a confidential letter can, without the consent of the author (or, if deceased, his representatives) give authority for its publication in order that the addressee can profit from the publication. To decide the issue, it was necessary to determine the effect of the act of gift of the letter; in short, was it a gift of the physical manuscript only, or of the manuscript and its contents? I argued strongly that only the manuscript was gifted, citing the English case of *Pope* v. *Curl* where it had been decided that the recipient of letters from Swift, Pope and others had arguably received a gift of the paper, but had not acquired a right to publish the letters to the world. I also asserted that the sons of Burns were most materially interested in maintaining their father's reputation. Moving once more into somewhat extravagant language, I claimed that, on the one hand, Clarinda was "safe from all obloquy, *stat nominis umbra*, she is concealed under a veil of impenetrable mystery", while on the other hand, publication of the content of the letters would injure and affect Burns's children.[3] I concluded that the family trusted that the court would give them reason to hope that the publication should never more be heard of, but quietly sink into that oblivion from which it should never have been drawn.

It would have been very helpful to our case had we been able to reveal the identity of Clarinda. Sir Walter Scott has given an account of how the letters came to be published in a letter dated 22nd January 1808 to Lady Abercorn:[4]

As Mrs Meiklehose [*sic*] advanced in years her vanity became rather too strong for her discretion and confiding in the charity of her confidants and in her own character as a sort of dévote, she thought fit to show this correspondence to particular friends and at length to a faithless young divine who sat up all night to make copies, put himself into the Glasgow mail coach with peep of day and sold all the amatory effusions of Sylvander and Clarinda to a Glasgow Bookseller for the moderate sum of ten guineas. To the great horror of poor Clarinda and the absolute confusion of all the Godly in Edinburgh forth came a sixpenny pamphlet containing all these precious productions. The Heroine of the piece being respectably connected the book was suppressed, partly by threatening and partly by bribing the bookseller.

I am afraid the facts are less prosaic than Sir Walter imagined. Mrs McLehose had been prevailed upon by some friends to lend the letters to a gentleman of the name of Finlay, who was engaged in writing a life of the poet, to enable Finlay to make a few extracts from the letters to enrich the account. Besides making use of the extracts, Finlay gave permission to Stewart & Macgoun to publish all the letters. The preface to this publication contained a number of falsehoods. I quote two sentences by way of illustration:[5]

We are happy, that, from the condescension of the Proprietor, we are enabled to favour the Public with an additional portion of the writings of our favourite Poet.

As the Editor is vested with the sole power to publish these letters, any other person presuming to Print them, will be prosecuted in terms of Law.

In fact, there was no condescension from Mrs McLehose, and she had granted no power to publish. Stewart & Macgoun knew they were on safe ground in alleging she had consented to publication, however, as they knew that Mrs McLehose wished to preserve her anonymity, and that she would not seek to restrain publication herself, as to do so she would necessitate revealing her identity. We therefore had to proceed without evidence from her.

The decision in the Stewart case was issued in May 1804. In the event, their Lordships did not find it necessary to decide the precise effect of the gift by Sylvander to Clarinda, contenting themselves with finding that communication in letters is always made under the implied confidence that they will not be published without the consent of the writer, and that Burns's representatives therefore had a sufficient interest, for the vindication of his literary character, to restrain the publication. It was perhaps surprising that Lord Craig gave an opinion in the case, as he was, of course, Clarinda's cousin, but I suppose he was seeking to protect the family name. Stewart & Macgoun lodged an appeal which was refused.

In 1803 I had been instructed to act once again on behalf of Cadell, Davies and Creech in relation to a publication by James Robertson, a printer in Edinburgh, of an edition of Burns's poetry entitled *Poems, Chiefly in the Scottish dialect, by Robert Burns, 1802*.

My clients claimed to be fully vested in all rights of publication (or in the alternative exclusive privilege) in these works. The basis of their claim was the Statute of Anne (1710), the first Act in the country and the world to give the courts copyright powers, whereas previously matters were regulated by the common law until the point of publication, whereupon the Stationers' Company in London had powers to control and potentially restrict the making of copies.

The Act is intended to achieve two objects. Firstly, to declare, in absolute terms, that an author, and those deriving title from him, should have an exclusive privilege of printing and reprinting his own works for the term of fourteen years from the date of publication; and, if the author is alive at the expiry of the first term of fourteen years, then for a further and final term of fourteen years. And, secondly, to set up a system of penalties and forfeitures against offenders, subject to various conditions, one of which is that the original publication should be registered in the Stationers' Hall.

Robertson's book contained not only the poems published in 1787, the copyright in which had expired in 1801, but also included poems pirated from the 1793 and 1800 editions. We had raised actions to stop the publication and Lord Meadowbank had granted the interim interdict we requested. Meadowbank had been a subscriber to Burns's first Edinburgh Edition, but so had many members of Faculty, and there was no reason for him to disqualify himself from hearing the case. We also raised an action claiming damages and expenses, and the actions were conjoined.

The case came before Lord Glenlee on 7th June 1803. Glenlee is the son of Sir Thomas Miller, the late Lord President, who made clear his disapproval of the Burns family. Glenlee ordered written arguments on the law to be submitted along with the parties' statements of facts, in order that he might report to the Inner House.

Robertson instructed Archibald Fletcher, the same counsel as was acting in the Stewart case. He had two grounds of defence, one based on a defect of title, and the other on a denial of any privilege on the part of my clients. I was able to counter these arguments, but in the end, the issue for decision was whether the fact that the editions of 1793 and 1800 had not been entered at Stationers' Hall was fatal to our case.

On report to the Inner House, it was decided that my clients were not entitled to restrain the publication of Robertson's edition on the ground that the Statute of Anne protected the copyright only if it had been registered with Stationers' Hall, so the interdict was recalled and the claim for damages dismissed. We took the case to appeal. The majority of the judges in the appeal were of the view that no protection was available to my clients and the family, again on the basis that neither the second Edinburgh Edition nor the 1800 Edition had been registered. The minority of two dissenting judges comprised Lords Meadowbank and Woodhouselee, both friends of Burns. It was unsurprising that Lord Meadowbank, who had granted the original interdict, was one of the judges who found in our favour. Lord Woodhouselee, the other judge who supported us, a lifelong friend of Burns, was satisfied that the common law of Scotland protected the copyright.

The case then went on appeal to the House of Lords, but a decision was issued only in 1811. Our appeal was allowed. Lord Chancellor Eldon explained that the majority of the judges in the Court of Session had misunderstood the statute. The correct view is that legal protection is given for two successive periods of fourteen years, but statutory penalties apply during only the first period. For the protection in the second period to be effective, holders of copyright must have a common law right to enforce, in the absence of statutory penalties. The views expressed by the two dissenting judges in the Court of Session were held to be correct.

Those decisions were important for Burns's family, and the income from the posthumous publications enabled the family to enjoy a more comfortable life than the poet himself enjoyed.

CHAPTER 21

MEMORIALS

FROM 1810

SIR WALTER SCOTT

Sir Walter Scott was born in Edinburgh in 1771, the fourth surviving child of Walter Scott, Writer to the Signet. He was educated at the High School of Edinburgh and the University of Edinburgh where he studied Classics. He joined his father's legal firm as an apprentice in 1786.

In 1787, he met Robert Burns for the first and only time.

With his father's approval, Scott decided to aim for the Bar, and enrolled in a Scots Law class at the University of Edinburgh in 1790–91. He was admitted to the Faculty of Advocates on 11th July 1792. During the early years of his practice he was instructed almost exclusively in the lower courts. His income from private practice was insufficient to support his family, and he was appointed Sheriff Depute of Selkirkshire on 16th December 1799.

On 2nd March 1801 Scott was initiated and passed and raised to the degree of Master Mason at Lodge St David, Edinburgh.

In 1806 Scott became one of the principal clerks of the Court of Session, a salaried post which he could combine with his post as Sheriff at Selkirk, thereby giving him a guaranteed income from the law without having to practise as an advocate.

He was bitterly opposed to electoral reform in Scotland.

Sir Walter Scott was created a baronet on 22nd April 1820. He became insolvent and signed a Trust Deed for his creditors in 1826. He died in 1832.

I am Sir Walter Scott. I am fifty-two years of age. I make this statement on 31st May 1824.

I met Robert Burns on only one occasion. This was in 1787, at Sciennes Hill House, the Edinburgh residence of Professor Adam Ferguson. He was part of a literary circle which included Professor Dugald Stewart, one of Burns's champions when he burst onto the Edinburgh scene, and Stewart may have invited Burns to one of Ferguson's soirées. In any event, I was there with my father and the Professor's son Adam, who was a school friend.

Burns was greatly affected by the scene depicted in a print by Bunbury on the wall in the Professor's salon. He actually shed tears, and asked if anyone could name the poet who had composed the piece which was inscribed under it:[1]

> Cold on Canadian hills or Minden's plain,
> Perhaps that parent mourned her soldier slain;
> Bent o'er her babe, her eye dissolved in dew,
> The big drops mingling with the milk he drew
> Gave the sad presage of his future years,
> The child of misery, baptized in tears.

I knew it to be John Langhorne, and whispered the answer to a friend who passed it on to Burns, and by the expression he gave me I could tell he was impressed!

I was called to the Bar on 11th July 1792, on the same day as my great friend William Clerk, the younger son of John Clerk of Eldin. William's brother John (later Lord Eldin) had been called in 1785. While studying for admission to the Faculty I had made many other friends who later became eminent: George Jos. Bell, who was called in 1791, was a polite but rather academic young man, less interested in socialising than my more outgoing contemporaries James Edmonstone,

George Abercromby, John Irving and David Boyle (now the Lord Justice Clerk), all of whom were called shortly after I was admitted.

It was only after Bell became involved in acting for Burns's family that I was apprised of the arrangements which Burns had made for the publication of his works. I must say Burns had been very badly advised. His contract with William Creech was leonine, though I consider that Creech treated Burns's family fairly after the poet's death. I have kept control of all aspects of the publication and printing of my own works, to considerable financial advantage. I have been able to secure advance payments of royalties and obtain credit on the strength of works as yet unwritten.

In October 1811, I was in correspondence with my friend Matthew Weld Hartstonge, the Irish poet and historical novelist. He had been to Dumfries and had seen the grave of Burns with its simple inscription composed by his widow Jean. I advised Matthew that in my opinion it was a disgrace to our country that something more worthy of Burns's fame had not been erected over his grave, but, although frequently proposed, it had uniformly fallen to the ground for want of subscriptions or from some disagreement about the nature of the monument to be erected.

I already knew something about the situation regarding Burns's grave in Dumfries. Dorothy Wordsworth, William's sister, had told me that on a trip to Scotland in 1803, she and William had visited Dumfries, and a local bookseller had offered to show them round the churchyard. He had pointed first to the spot where Burns was buried, marked only by a plain stone, and then, by way of contrast, to an adjoining grand monument to a local lawyer. He had told Dorothy that Burns had written many a lampoon about the lawyer, yet for all Burns's achievements, that was how they both now lay. That, I think, inspired William to write his poem 'To the Sons of Burns',[2] the concluding verse of which is rather ominous:

Let no mean hope your souls enslave;
Be independent, generous, brave;
Your Father such example gave,
And such revere;
But be admonished by his grave,
And think, and fear!

In November 1813 William Grierson, a local businessman in Dumfries, who also thought that Robert Burns's grave in St Michael's churchyard should be marked by something more notable than a plain stone slab, circulated to a number of prominent persons in Dumfriesshire a letter[3] which canvassed support for the construction of a lasting monument:

> It has long been a subject of regret and indeed a reflection against Scotland, that nothing yet has been done to perpetuate the memory, and do honour to the genius of its native bard, Robert Burns, by marking the spot where his ashes rest. There can be no doubt that, if a public subscription was opened, under the management of a respectable committee, a very liberal sum would soon be procured, in aid of that already promised from abroad, to erect a Monument at his grave, in St Michael's Churchyard, Dumfries. A few of the friends and admirers of Burns having lately taken the affair into consideration, concluded that the most proper method would be to invite a meeting of such gentlemen as might be disposed to promote the measure, to take place in the George Inn on Thursday, the 16th December, at two o'clock afternoon, in order to name a committee, and to adopt such resolutions as may appear best calculated to carry into effect so desirable an object. It is therefore hoped you will find it convenient to attend the meeting on the above mentioned day.

Eighteen people attended the meeting. Grierson and the Reverend Henry Duncan were appointed joint secretaries. They were instructed to contact various friends and acquaintances of the late poet. Although I had met Burns but once, I was included among those who received an appeal for assistance.

In reply to Grierson I confirmed that I was very much obliged to the Committee for affording me an opportunity of testifying my high veneration for the Ayrshire Bard. I felt the honour to Burns had been too long delayed, perhaps until some parts of his character were forgotten by those amongst whom he lived. At the time, my circle of friends was very limited, but I hoped to get some subscriptions. I asked Grierson to send me a list of such subscriptions as had already been procured, so that I might have some general rule for assisting my friends, for I had previously observed that it was often advantageous to have an idea of what would be thought liberal and handsome. I put my name down for ten guineas without limiting myself to that sum, however, should there be further occasion for contributions. I passed on the papers which Grierson had sent me to Archibald Constable, the bookseller, whose influence was considerable, in the hope that it might open some avenues to which I had not personally any access.

I wrote to a number of friends seeking subscriptions, pointing out that there were few of us who did not owe a guinea or two to his memory for the pleasure that his works had afforded us. Among others, Matthew Hartstonge himself made a contribution of £5. Later in the year I organised, in conjunction with my friends Mr and Mrs Henry Siddons, owners of the Edinburgh Theatre, an evening of a good play and farce in support of the appeal. It took place on 13th December 1813. We had a very genteel, if by no means crowded, audience. The boxes in particular were filled with fashionable people, but neither the pit nor the gallery was as full as I should have expected they might have been from the name of the Bard. My wife Charlotte took two boxes, and used all the influence she had with her friends, of whom several took boxes and filled them well. So if the returns did not quite equal our zeal and my expectations, it was not our fault.

The net profit from the evening was £40, to which Henry and Harriet Siddons generously added a personal contribution of ten guineas. I felt keenly what I regarded as the failure of the event. It brought home to me just how little influence I could reckon upon in Edinburgh society, for I had assailed every friend I thought I had in support of the occasion.

It took a long time to raise the funds required for the monument. I felt that some organisations were less than generous. Burns's principal Masonic connection was with Lodge Canongate Kilwinning in Edinburgh, and, owing to the status and means of the members, one might have expected the Lodge to be in a position to make a handsome donation. My father and brother had been initiated and passed and raised at that Lodge. But in the event, their subscription was only twenty guineas, which was a great disappointment to the Committee.

The whole project for the Mausoleum became embroiled in legal disputes. Fortunately, these difficulties were dealt with in Dumfries, and I was not involved in advising Grierson, who had to cope with the histrionics of the architect, sculptor and contractors. However, Grierson let me know later what he had been required to deal with.

In response to an advertisement, over fifty designs for the monument were received, and on 25th April 1815, the plans of Gavin Hunt, a London architect, were approved. Estimates for the work were obtained, and that of John Milligan, Dumfries, amounting to just over £331, was accepted. On 30th May 1815 there was a meeting at the locus, after which it was decided, with the agreement of Mrs Jean Burns, that the site of the grave holding Burns and his sons

Francis-Wallace and Maxwell was too closely surrounded by existing monuments and tombstones, and therefore that the project would involve moving the remains to a more suitable open location. A site was soon selected, and on 5th June 1815, after the laying of the foundation stone, Grierson attended a meeting with the Committee, when he met the architect Gavin Hunt and the sculptor Peter Turnerelli, both of whom had travelled from London.

Turnerelli is an outstanding sculptor. Born in Belfast, the grandson of an Italian political refugee, he trained at the Royal Academy and, at the age of twenty-four, acted as instructor to the King's daughters before being appointed Sculptor-in-Ordinary to the Royal Family. Turnerelli said the sculpture would take two years to execute, and, somewhat to Grierson's surprise, Turnerelli agreed that, should the funds raised not reach the amount necessary to cover the total cost, he would bear any risk in the event of there being a shortfall, in that he was determined to raise funds in London to support the project.

Grierson was present on 19th September 1815 at the exhumation and re-interment necessary for the Memorial project to proceed. The coffins of Francis-Wallace and Maxwell did not disintegrate, and were easily transported to the new location. Burns's coffin was of poorer quality and, unfortunately, as the wood was being reinforced, the body separated into dust and bones, which required to be placed in a new coffin. The process was carried out with considerable dignity, but those who were there were greatly affected.

As with almost every building project from time immemorial, there were problems with the contractor. Grierson was often in despair, as to both the workmanship and the materials used; according to the Committee, the contractor was skimping on the thickness and quality of the stone being used. Eventually the architect had to intervene to try to ensure the contractor adhered to the contract, but to no avail. There were disputes, references to arbitration, and defamatory exchanges of correspondence.

Even the fund-raising efforts were not without controversy. Subscriptions were received at a commemoration dinner held in London on 25th May 1816, over which the Earl of Aberdeen presided, where the income was £528 but the "expenses" amounted to £308, leaving only £220. The Committee had difficulty extracting even this amount from a Mr Jardine, the collector, and in the end, it was only after intervention by a London agent that the sum was recovered and paid to Turnerelli as a first payment to account of the contract price of the sculpture. After an acrimonious exchange of correspondence between the Committee and Turnerelli, the sculptor reluctantly sent the sculpture to Dumfries in 1819. He had been promised an additional £150 from a collection in Demerara; I do not think he ever received any payment for his work beyond that £150 and the £220 raised at the London dinner. He maintained he was due at least £800 for the commission, but he seems to have lost interest in pursuing the matter in 1821, according to Grierson.

Other monuments were, of course, raised to Burns, and I contributed £5 to the Alloway Monument and two guineas to the Edinburgh Monument.

I have had other involvements with maintaining the memory of Burns. On Thursday 25th January 1816, marking the anniversary of his birth, a splendid dinner was held at MacEwan's Tavern in the Royal Exchange, Edinburgh, attended by many friends and admirers of the poet. Alexander Boswell of Auchinleck took the Chair, and I acted as one of the stewards, assisted by George Thomson, Burns's collaborator on *Select Scottish Airs*. It was a marathon feast of fine food and wine, lasting from six o'clock in the evening until two o'clock on the Friday morning. Among the many toasts, one was to me, proposed among what was described in the press as pealing applause. To this, I made a happy and ingenious reply.

Burns has been criticised for his appeals for patronage to obtain preferment and promotion within the Excise. I deem that unfair, as I myself have attempted to second the views of friends when seeking advancement. Some years ago I had hopes of securing nomination as a candidate for the situation of Baron of Exchequer, and sought the patronage of the Duke of Buccleuch. Sadly the Duke found himself unable to interfere with the distribution of patronage, and I renounced any notion of holding a high judicial office.

Owing to illness, I was unable to be present at the public dinner in honour of Burns held in Edinburgh on 22nd February 1819. It was well attended, however, by about 300 guests. This was the first dinner in Edinburgh at which the Whig element felt confident enough to speak at a public occasion, after their travails of the previous two decades. According to reports, Henry Mackenzie spoke warmly of his association with Burns when he first arrived in Edinburgh. I was sad to miss the dinner; I would have added some Tory balance to the evening.

It was interesting that, only a year later, radicalism reared itself from slumber in Scotland when strikes were called. I must concede that some of those who joined the strikes were in desperate circumstances; for example, the wages paid to weavers halved between 1816 and 1819, meaning they received about ten shillings per week. But nothing can excuse an uprising against the Crown. Following the deaths in Manchester at what has come to be known as the Peterloo Massacre, a rally *in memoriam* was held in Paisley in September 1819. This led to the formation of a plot for insurrection, and in April 1820 various skirmishes took place at Bonnymuir and in the west of the country, which the yeomanry suppressed with ease.

Courts of Oyer and Terminer were convened in Glasgow and Stirling to prosecute the ringleaders for treason. Despite pleas for mercy, three were hanged and beheaded, and others transported to penal colonies. Following these convictions, what was known as the 'Radical War' petered out.

I was, however, exercised by the plight of the weavers, and arranged the formation of a committee of gentlemen to oversee the employment of some of these destitute and disaffected men in the construction of a pathway round Salisbury Craigs in Holyrood Park, one of my favourite haunts. This pathway has come to be known as the Radical Road, which name does not have my approbation.

The country is now stable, and I feel I may lay claim to having contributed to the improvement. My former schoolmate and great friend Robert Dundas, Second Viscount Melville, and I made all the arrangements for the hugely successful visit of George IV to Scotland in 1822. This was the first visit of a reigning monarch since 1707, and the glorious reception the King received had the effect of greatly weakening the radical element in Scottish society. In the course of the King's visit my school friend Adam Ferguson, now a distinguished military man, was knighted at Hopetoun House.

Robert is the son of the late Henry Dundas, who died in 1811. Henry had in effect ruled Scotland for over twenty years, and was made Viscount Melville in 1802, but his political career had ended with controversy, and the outcome involved Harry Erskine's brother Tom, a barrister greatly admired by Burns. Tom, who died last year, was the youngest of the Erskine brothers. His eldest brother is David, 11th Earl of Buchan and former Grand Master of the Grand Lodge of Scotland, and his other brother was the late Harry, the advocate and Whig agitator, the best-natured man I ever knew, and with but one fault – he could not say no – and thus sometimes misled those who trusted him. Tom was a brilliant lawyer, but I regarded him as positively mad.

Over the years Melville repeatedly crossed swords with Harry and

Tom. The culmination of this occurred when Tom, who had been appointed Lord Chancellor in the Ministry of All the Talents, formed in 1806 following William Pitt's death, presided over the impeachment of Melville for misappropriation of public money. The way in which Tom conducted the case was greatly admired. Although Melville was acquitted, he was thereafter excluded from public office, and died in 1811. At the time of his death he was still plotting, his last intrigue being to ensure that Harry Erskine did not become a judge in the Court of Session! For all his faults, and he had many, I stand by my comment after his death that the country had lost a patriot whose like she will not see for a century to come.

I was entertained when I learned of the reaction Burns had to Melville's attributing to him the ditty he penned about the reel dancing of Jane, the late Duchess of Gordon. She had a vivacious personality, and while she was often a guest at my Edinburgh home, I did try to keep my distance from her, which from time to time displeased her, as I avoided attending many of her parties. She was one of many who were entranced by Burns, and she confided in me that he was the only man whose conversation alone could carry her into ecstasy.

After Jane's death I was happy to tell my friends that in my opinion her sole claim to wit rested on her brazen impudence and disregard to the feelings of all who were near her. Inability to take a joke is the feature of a bully, and that was illustrated by her hounding out of the country of James Ogilvy, seventh Earl of Findlater and fourth Earl of Seafield. Apparently a ship had been constructed in an innovative way, with copper sheathing on its underside to prevent deterioration of the timbers. It was launched with the name the *Duchess of Gordon*. Ogilvy remarked that he had always known that the Duchess had a brass neck and a brazen face, but had been unaware that she had a copper arse. The Duchess raised court proceedings against him, and Ogilvy fled to Saxony, never to return to Scotland.

I am irritated by the criticism of my having voted against Harry Erskine in the contested election for the Dean of Faculty in 1796. As a Tory, I felt I had no choice but to support Robert Dundas, the Lord Advocate, nephew of Henry. The issue divided friendships. If you consider my circle of friends, my confidant, the late William Erskine, and Edmonstone, Abercromby and Boyle, all voted for Dundas, whereas Irving and the Clerk brothers voted for Erskine. Bell voted for Dundas, but I think he later regretted doing so.

I am distressed by the lack of recognition William Erskine received. He was not related to the Whig Erskines. He was a gifted advocate, and not long after calling, he assisted Robert Hamilton in defending the traitor Robert Watt in 1794. I note that the trials of Watt and Downie are referred to in previous statements. I watched Watt's trial from seven in the morning until two the following morning. Watt was a scoundrel, but William and Robert did their best for him. I actually attended Watt's execution, and at the time wrote to my friend, Mrs Christian Rutherford:[4]

> I stayed a single day in town, to witness the exit of the ci-devant Jacobin, Mr Watt. It was a very solemn scene, but the pusillanimity of the unfortunate victim was astonishing, considering the boldness of his nefarious plans. It is a matter of regret that his associate Downie should have received a reprieve.

William Erskine died last year, after only six months on the bench as Lord Kilkeddar. He had been passed over for elevation for years for no good reason. As I wrote to my friend Joanna Baillie at that time:[5]

> I did indeed rejoice at Erskine's promotion. There is a degree of melancholy attending the later stage of a barrister's professions which, though no one cares for

sentimentalities attendant on a man of fifty or thereabout, in a rusty black bombazine gown, are not the less cruelly felt; their business sooner or later fails, for younger men will work cheaper, and longer, and harder–besides that the cases are few, comparatively, in which senior counsel are engaged, and it is not etiquette to ask any one in that advanced age to take the whole burden of a cause. Insensibly, without decay of talent, and without losing the public esteem, there is a gradual decay of employment, which almost no man ever practised thirty years without experiencing; and thus the honours and dignities of the Bench, so hardly earned, and themselves leading but to toils of another kind, are peculiarly desirable. Erskine would have sat there ten years ago, but for wretched intrigues.

There has been a great deal of misunderstanding concerning my attitude to Burns. I could accept his rather romantic and sentimental view of the past, though his flirtation with Jacobitism belonged to fancy rather than reason. It is impossible to divine his attitude to the Union; at some periods he seems to condemn it but in other writings, mostly towards the end of his life, he gives strong support to it.

His political views in general seemed to change dramatically. In the mid 1780s his sympathies lay with Pitt, who had promoted a reform bill which, if passed, would have extended the franchise. But by the beginning of 1789, I believe Pitt's conservatism caused Burns to change his allegiance to the Whigs in the form of Charles Fox, who appeared to offer a real prospect of reform. In Dumfries his associates Riddell, Syme, Fergusson, McCraken and Maxwell, were all liberal reformers. When the Tory backlash to seditious unrest occurred, mindful of his position in the Excise, Burns largely kept his views to himself, hiding behind the cloak of anonymity in anything he did publish.

Burns did, however, produce great works, and, sadly, I regret that my own poetic efforts do not bear comparison with his. I do regard him, nonetheless, as the unfortunate primer of what has been described as the subsequent deluge of peasant poets. As I once put it in an article in the *Edinburgh Annual Register* for 1808:

> the success of Burns had the effect of exciting general emulation among all of his class in Scotland that were able to tag a rhyme. Poets began to chirp like grasshoppers in a sunshine day. The steep rocks poured down poetical goatherds, and the bowels of the earth vomited forth rhyming colliers.

So far as Burns's character is concerned, I think he has been unfairly maligned recently by most commentators. His superiors described him as a man who might be considered a credit to the Excise, and as someone who gave it the most unremitting attention.

As regards his legacy to the world, his literary contribution, I see Burns in the same luminescence as my friend Lord Byron, whose recent death, also at the age of thirty-seven, has so shocked me. I believe that although they were from completely different backgrounds, they shared many attributes. I met Lord Byron on numerous occasions in London, and we enjoyed many a tête-à-tête. Our sentiments agreed a great deal, except upon the subject of politics. From what I wrote about Byron to my friend Mr Moore, you will readily see the similarity to Burns:[6]

> He used to espouse a high strain of what is now called Liberalism, but it appeared to me that the pleasure it afforded him, as a vehicle for displaying his wit and

satire against individuals in office, was at the bottom of this habit of thinking, rather than any real conviction of the political principles on which he talked.

In my appreciation of Lord Byron, I wrote:

> It is not now the question, what were Byron's faults, what his mistakes; but how is the blank which he has left in British literature to be filled up? Not, we fear, in one generation, which, among many highly gifted persons, has produced none who approached Byron in ORIGINALITY, the first attribute of genius. Only thirty-seven years old – so much already done for immortality – so much time remaining, as it seemed to us short-sighted mortals, to maintain and to extend his fame, and to atone for errors in conduct and levities in composition: who will not grieve that such a race has been shortened, though not always keeping the straight path, such a light extinguished, though sometimes flaming to dazzle and to bewilder?

These attributes – originality, the ability to dazzle and bewilder – were shared by Burns. Lord Byron himself was of the opinion that the rank of Burns was the very first of his art. In my opinion, no poet, with the exception of Shakespeare, has ever possessed Burns's power to inspire the most varied and discordant emotions from his works.

Later

The arrangements contrived by Scott for the printing and publication of his works involved him being a secret partner in two partnerships with the brothers James and John Ballantyne. These partnerships printed and published Scott's works, and obtained substantial loans to finance distributions to Scott which he used to meet his extravagant expenditure at Abbotsford, on the house and estate. Scott obtained private loans from friends by claiming he was only a lender to these partnerships, and that the partnerships were temporarily unable to repay him. In reality, he was a principal of the partnerships.

When the partnerships were unable to pay their debts in 1826, Scott faced insolvency. Perhaps aware of his impending precarious financial position, he had transferred Abbotsford to a trust for himself and his son, under which Scott reserved a liferent to himself, with the fee going to his son on Scott's death. At a meeting of his creditors it was disclosed that he had assets of £48,494 and liabilities of £104,081. He signed a Trust Deed for Creditors on the basis that his continuing royalties would be paid to his creditors until his liabilities were discharged. His creditors were persuaded by Scott's friends, including Sandie Young, not to seek to invalidate the transfer of Abbotsford to the trust, so Scott was able to remain in occupation of the estate until his death.

After Scott died, his family, with the assistance of the publisher Robert Cadell, paid off the balance of Scott's liability and obtained a Discharge in 1833.

CHAPTER 22

POSTSCRIPT

1836

ANDREW McLEHOSE

Andrew McLehose was the son of Burns's friend, Mrs Agnes McLehose. He was born in Glasgow in 1778 and, following his parents' separation, moved to Edinburgh with his mother.

He was apprenticed to Robert Ainslie WS and was himself admitted a Writer to the Signet in 1808.

Andrew McLehose married in 1809. He inherited a substantial amount from the estate of his mother's cousin, Lord Craig, in 1813.

He died in 1839 having been predeceased by his wife and two of his children. His mother survived him. Two years after her death, in 1843 her grandson William, son of Andrew, published the correspondence between Agnes ('Clarinda') McLehose and Burns.

My name is Andrew McLehose. I am a lawyer. I am sixty years of age. I am the son of Robert Burns's friend Mrs Agnes McLehose, known to lovers of Burns as 'Clarinda'. I make this statement on 30th June 1838; it should not be made public until after my mother's death.

I consider I am uniquely placed to reflect on the involvement of Robert Burns with my mother, and Burns's opinion of the legal profession. I should also comment on how two issues which greatly exercised Burns – the French revolutionary wars and the extension of the franchise – were resolved.

Great Britain's war with the French continued after Burns died until the Treaty of Amiens was signed in 1802. In the event, the peace lasted only about a year, as the Napoleonic Wars commenced in 1803 ending only after Waterloo in 1815. Meaningful electoral reform was not achieved in Scotland until 1832 on the enactment of the Scottish Reform Act. Before 1832, Members of Parliament were elected at a meeting of representatives from each burgh, and the total electorate in Scotland was only about 4,000. The electorate was increased more than sixteen fold by the Act, and now individual votes are added up across each constituency. The franchise is now extended to householders of £10 annual value in the burghs, and property owners of £10 or tenants of £50 rental in the country constituencies. Of course, it can hardly be described as a universal suffrage – the population of Scotland is about two million, and only about 65,000 males can vote.

I often wonder how Burns, had he survived, would have reacted to the poem about Thomas Muir which I believe was composed by the advocate John MacFarlane of Kirkton. He was the son of the Reverend John MacFarlane, minister of the Canongate Kirk in Edinburgh, and was admitted to the Faculty of Advocates two years after Muir. They were close friends. Muir was of course sufficiently true to his liberal principles to be an agitator for reform, and he had suffered the dire consequence of death at the young age of thirty-three. MacFarlane wrote:

> Doomed from this mansion to a foreign land;
> To waste his days of gay and sprightly youth;
> And all for sowing with a liberal hand
> The seeds of that seditious libel – Truth.[1]

I suspect Burns would have been uneasy about that metaphor, bearing in mind his farming background and his failure clearly to support the cause of reform.

Burns's equivocal attitude to reform has been the subject of much criticism, mostly from people who never met him. I consider the best insight was given in the letter from James Gray which was reproduced in the 1815 edition of *The Life and Works of Burns* by Alexander Peterkin. Gray was a Master at the High School in Edinburgh, but he had known Burns well, and, as Latin teacher and Headmaster of Dumfries Academy, had taught Burns's children. His view was that while Burns was an advocate of constitutional reform, he was never involved in what he described as "the mad cry of revolution".

As regards my family, after my parents' wedding in 1786, they lived in Glasgow where my father James was in practice as a lawyer. It was not a happy marriage. I believe my father was cruel to mother and they separated in 1790. My father went to London where he dissipated his fortune and was gaoled for debt. Mother was fortunate in that my maternal grandfather supported her and his grandchildren until his death.

My father's family paid off his London debts on condition that he left the country. He went to Jamaica where he died in 1812.

After my grandfather died, Mother had decided to move to Edinburgh where she had family support from her cousin William Craig, at the time a successful advocate. We knew him as 'Uncle William'. He was later elevated to the Bench as Lord Craig. A huge amount of ill-informed speculation has abounded about the nature of my mother's relationship with Burns. I know that Uncle William strongly disapproved, and Lord President Glenlee was of a similar view. I have no hesitation in saying that theirs was a platonic friendship, no more than that. When Burns used to call at our house, the children or other guests were always present and, so far as I am aware, they never met alone elsewhere.

I have another source for my view. Burns's greatest friend while he was in Edinburgh was Robert Ainslie, Writer to the Signet, and he was introduced to my mother by Burns. After Burns moved to Dumfries, Ainslie became a close confidant of my mother, and he was categoric that there was nothing untoward between my mother and Burns. At the time, Burns was conducting an illicit relationship with our servant, Jenny Clow. Poor Jenny! She died shortly after giving birth to Burns's child. My mother did dismiss her, of course, when her pregnancy became apparent, but I believe she did all she could to look after her in her last days.

I know that my mother was much shocked when she heard of Burns's marriage to Jean Armour, as this outcome was so much at variance with what had passed between her and Burns previously.

Ainslie was kind enough to indenture me as his apprentice in his practice, which was of considerable benefit to me, almost as much as the bequest I received from Uncle William's estate in 1813!

I was eighteen years of age in 1796 when Burns died, and I was immediately aware of my mother's anxiety about letters she had sent to Burns during his time in Edinburgh. She enlisted the help of Robert Ainslie in recovering these letters. I have read these letters and I am inclined to agree with the late Sir Walter Scott's opinion that they are the most extraordinary mixture of sense and nonsense, and of love human and divine, that was ever exposed to the eye of the world. Ainslie has lately distanced himself from my mother. I know he has had financial troubles, and has become very religious. Perhaps my mother reminds him of a period in his life he would rather forget. My mother thinks some of Burns's poetic genius has rubbed off on her, and has taken to composing verse. One Christmas, Ainslie left his card at our home, and mother sent him a poem:[2]

> Full many a Christmas have I seen,
> But ne'er saw this before—
> One's dear and always welcome friend
> A card leave at the door.
>
> Such ceremony sure bespeaks
> A friendship in the wane:
> Friendship, dear tie, when once it breaks,
> It seldom knits again.
>
> Then fare-ye-well, my once dear friend,
> And happy may you be;
> May all your future hours be blest
> Like those you've spent with me!

My mother is now very elderly but she still speaks kindly of Burns. About ten years ago she had a social meeting with Sir Walter Scott and Mrs Jean Burns in Edinburgh. I cannot imagine what they discussed!

In her journal, under the date 6th December 1831, my mother wrote:[3]

This day I never can forget. Parted with Burns in the year 1791, never more to meet in this world. Oh, may we meet in Heaven!

Burns's widow survived him by thirty-eight years. She died in 1834, and under her Will she left £100 to her granddaughter Elizabeth, daughter of her son Robert; the family Bible and the poet's books to Robert; portraits to each of her sons, William-Nicol and James; and her clothing in specific bequests to her sisters. The remainder of her estate passed to her granddaughter Sarah, daughter of her son James, explaining that she was favouring her over Elizabeth because Sarah had no other protector in Great Britain but herself.

Burns enjoyed support and friendship from members of the legal profession throughout his brief life. Among his best and closest friends were Gavin Hamilton, John Richmond, David Cathcart, Robert Ainslie, Harry Erskine, Fraser Tytler, Alexander Cunningham and John Syme. Lord Monboddo greatly admired him. Robert Aiken and Gavin Hamilton were leading subscribers to the Kilmarnock Edition and about 200 lawyers subscribed to the Edinburgh Edition. Of course, some lawyers thought him a liberal cad; you would number Lords Glenlee, Craig and Dreghorn and Alexander Young of Harburn among them.

After his death, lawyers were the leading lights in providing support for his impoverished family. Cunningham and Syme led the way, with William Thomson of Moat managing funds for his children, and Professor Bell protecting the family's financial interests.

I am driven to the conclusion that in spite of his frequent denigration of lawyers, Burns secretly held them in high esteem.

Post postscript

Andrew McLehose died on 10th April 1839. He did not leave a Will. His estate had a value of £50, including the reversion in a fund of £1,000 set up by Lord Craig under his Will for the benefit of his mother, known forever as 'Clarinda'.

'Clarinda' died on 22nd October 1841; she also left no Will. The capital of the £1,000 fund and her personal estate, including manuscript letters between Robert Burns and her (valued at £25), passed to her grandson, William Craig McLehose, who promptly published the letters and a retrospect of his grandmother's life.

APPENDIX I

SUBMISSION
and
DECREET ARBITRAL

- - - - - -

William Burns and Jos. Norman

- - - - - -

The parties afternamed viz. William Burns in Lochlie on the one part and Joseph Norman, Seedsman in Ayr on the other part have Submitted and Required and hereby Submit and Referr all Clags Claims Pleas Processes of law debates differences and others whatsoever that presently subsist between them or that the one party can lay to the Charge of the other preceding the date hereof and particularly any claim of rent the said William Burns has against the said Joseph Norman for these four acres of land or thereby at Alloway the property of the said William Burns the possession of which the said Joseph Norman has of the date hereof Renounced, and also any claim of damage the said Joseph Norman has against the said William Burns and that to the amicable sentence friendly determination and Decreet Arbitral to be given furth and pronounced in the premises by David McClure, Merchant in Ayr and John McKenzie, Vintner there, Arbiters mutually chosen by both parties and in case of their variance, to an oversman to be chosen by them, with power to the said Arbiters or oversman to take all manner of probation by writ, witnesses or oath of parties which they shall think necessary, and to give furth and pronounce their Decreet Arbitral in the premises betwixt and the day of next, with power to the said Arbiters or oversman to prorogate this submission from time to time as they shall see necessary and Lastly both parties Bind and oblige themselves their heirs and successors to fulfill perform and abide by whatever is determined by the said Arbiters or oversman in the premises under the penalty of ten pounds Stg. to be paid by the party faillier to the other observing or willing to observe the same at our performance Consenting to the Registration hereof and of the Decreet Arbitral to be pronounced hereon in the Books of Council and Session or others competent that all Execution pass hereon, and constitute Mr David Rae, Advocate procurator In witness whereof both parties have subscribed these presents wrote upon this and the preceding pages of stampt paper by William Chalmers writer in Edinburgh at Ayr the twenty third day of April MDCC and seventy nine before these witnesses David Lamont writer in Ayr, John McCulloch, merchant and the said William Chalmers.

David Lamont, Witness   William Burns
John McCulloch, Witness   Jos. Norman
William Chalmers, Witness

Prorogated by several prorogations till April MDCC and eighty two, we Mr David McClure, merchant in Ayr and John McKenzie, vintner there, Arbiters mutually chosen by William Burns in Lochlie and Joseph Norman, Seedsman in Ayr conform to Submission entered into betwixt them of date the twenty third of April MDCC and seventy nine whereby the said parties submitted and referred all Clags Claims Pleas Processes of law debates differences and others whatsoever that then subsisted between them or that the one party could lay to the Charge of the other preceding the said date and particularly any claim of rent the said William Burns had against the said Joseph Norman for these four acres of land or thereby at Alloway the property of the said William Burns and also any Claim of Damage the said Joseph Norman had against the said William Burns.

Having Considered the process formerly raised before the Sheriff at said William Burns' instance against Joseph Norman for payment of said rent, the Memorials offered to us by both parties and proof adduced by said Joseph Norman, and heard parties, and we being therewith well and ripely advised and having God and a good conscience before our Eyes

Do give furth and pronounce our Decreet Arbitral in the said matter as follows, viz.

We find the said Joseph Norman has not proved his defence and find that the said William Burns has proved his defence and find that the said William Burns has proved by the said Joseph Norman's Admission that he entered to the possession of the lands in August seventeen hundred and seventy seven and ploughed part of them for Crop seventeen hundred and seventy eight and that the said William Burns or any in his name had not the possession thereof thereafter until the date of the said Submission,

Therefore,

We Decern and ordain the said Joseph Norman to make payment to the said William Burns of the sum of twelve pounds Stg. in full of all claim of rent and others whatsoever which he had against the said Joseph Norman preceding the date of the said Submission and that against the twenty eight day of December next seventeen hundred and eighty one years with interest thereof thereafter and till paid and upon payment being made we Decern both parties to discharge each other of all debatable matters subsisting between them on the said twenty third day of April seventeen hundred and seventy nine of which in the event foresaid we declare they are hereby discharged and further decern the said Joseph Norman to make payment to the said William Burns of twelve shillings and sixpence Sterling as his half of the expence of the said Submission and procedure thereon he being instantly ordained to pay William Chalmers, writer in Ayr, our clerk thereto, the sum of one pound five shillings Stg. and we ordain both parties to implement and perform their several parts of the premises to each other under the penalty mentioned in the said Submission. And we ordain this our Decreet Arbitral to be registered along with and in terms of the Clause of Registration contained in said Submission In witness whereof we have subscribed these presents consisting of this and the preceding page wrote by the said William Chalmers at Ayr the eight day of

November MDCC and eighty one Before these witnesses Colin McPhail, servant to the said John McKenzie and the said William Chalmers.

Colin McPhail, Witness
Wm. Chalmers, Witness

David McClure
Jn. McKenzie

APPENDIX II

DECREET ARBITRAL

- - - - - -

David McClure and William Burns

- - - - - -

I, JOHN HAMILTON Esquire of Sundrum, Umpire elected and nominated by James Grieve, in Boghead, and Charles Norval, Gairdner at Coilsfleld, conform to the powers given them in the Submission between David McClure of Shawwood, Merchant in Air, and William Burns in Lochlie, of date the twenty fourth day of September last, in which they were appointed Arbiters, but could not agree in their opinion, as appears from a Minute upon the back of said Submission, wherein I am appointed Umpire as above, of date the ninth day of April last,

Having accepted of the said office of Umpire or Oversman, and having considered the said Submission with the Claims and Memorials upon the points in dispute given in by both Parties, proof adduced by them, writings produced, heard the Parties, and inspected the farm of Lochlie mentioned in the Submission, And being upon the whole matter well and ripely advised, having God and a good conscience before my eyes,

Give furth and pronounce my Decreet arbitral as follows:

I Find that sometime in the year seventeen hundred and seventy six the said David McClure and William Burns bargained for a lease of the said farm of Lochlie for thirty eight years, in presence of Doctor John Campbell of Air, which bargain proceeded on a previous one for the same farm; That by the said previous bargain William Burns was to enter into possession at Martinmas seventeen hundred and seventy seven, but by the last he was to enter at Martinmas seventeen hundred and seventy six; That by the first he was to pay fifteen shillings Stg. per acre yearly for the first eight years and twenty shillings Stg. per acre yearly for the remaining thirty years of the lease, And by the second bargain was to pay twenty shillings Stg. per acre yearly from his entry at said term of Martinmas seventeen hundred and seventy six; That the said farm was to be inclosed, sub-divided, and limed by said David McClure at the rate of one hundred bolls of lime per acre, and also the said William Burns was to be allowed twelve Tons of limestone at Cairnhill lime quarry for each acre of said farm as a second dressing, and one shilling per ton for coals to burn the same; That said farm consists of one hundred and thirty acres, besides the mill damb for which William Burns was to be allowed lime, limestone & Coals in the same proportion, and was to pay rent at the same rate as for the rest of the farm per acre, providing the said miln damb was sufficiently drained to him; That said William Bums was to receive a compensation for his entering to the payment of twenty shillings Stg. per acre as by the second bargain in place of fifteen shillings Stg. per acre as by the first bargain yearly for the first eight years of said lease; And that William Burns entered into possession at Martinmas seventeen hundred and seventy six, in consequence of this said second agreement;

   Therefore I Find him entitled to retain out of the rents in his hands a sum equal to that advance rent which, after a calculation made by David Scott, Accountant to Messrs Hunters and Co., Bankers in Air, to whom I remitted this point for my information, I Fix and Determine to be two hundred and ten pounds one shilling and six pence Stg., and I allow the said William Burns to retain the same accordingly;

   I Also Find That the whole of the one hundred and thirty acres, exclusive of the mill damb, has been limed conform to bargain, excepting twenty six acres, for which **I** Find that the said William Burns entitled to an allowance at the rate of eight pence Stg. per boll for his liming the same, and therefore I allow the said William Burns to retain out of the rents of said farm the sum of eighty six pounds thirteen shillings and four pence Stg. as the value of two thousand six hundred bolls of lime at eight pence per boll for liming the said twenty six acres; But in regard the said William Burns has limed these twenty six acres out of seven hundred and twenty six tons of limestone delivered to him, and coals at one shilling Stg. per ton for burning the same (as herein after allowed him), being part of what has been furnished by the said David McClure for the second dressing of the said farm,

Therefore I Decern and Ordain the said William Burns to lay upon the said land for the second dressing against the term of Lambass seventeen hundred and eighty four, two thousand six hundred bolls of lime at his own charge, and produce vouchers thereof; Find That the farm has been inclosed and subdivided by said David McClure, excepting some dykes made by said William Burns, for the expence of which I find him entitled to have credit, and hereby allow him to retain on that account eighteen pounds ten shillings Stg., conform to vouchers shown to me, And Also to have credit for building houses and for grass seeds for ten acres of land the first year of the tack, amounting the said houses to seventy pounds eighteen shillings and six pence Stg. (David McClure having built a barn equal to twenty nine pounds one shilling and six pence Stg., which makes up the sum of one hundred pounds Stg. agreed to be laid out upon houses) and the grass seeds to ten pounds Stg. for both of which sums, amounting to eighty pounds eighteen shillings and six pence Stg., the said William Burns is hereby allowed retention;

I Find no rent chargeable for the ground occupied by the damb until it shall be drained, and that the said William Burns has no claim for damages by its not being drained;

I Find upon the Whole that the charge against the said William Burns at Whitsunday seventeen hundred and eighty two, the term immediately preceding the date of this Submission, is seven hundred and seventy five pounds Stg. and all the public burdens, being five and one half years rent at one hundred and thirty pounds Stg. yearly, Supposing him, the said William Burns, to have paid the public burthens, and, if otherwise, find him liable to refund to David McClure the whole or whatever part of them he has paid for the farm of Lochlie during William Burns's tack, besides said sum of seven hundred and seventy five pounds Stg., which includes said rent and sixty pounds Stg. for labouring thirty acres of limed land above the half of the farm the first year which William Burns states in his account to his own debit at two pounds Stg. per acre;

But I Find That from the said sum of seven hundred and seventy five pounds Stg. the said William Burns must have credit for the five articles before specified, for which he is allowed retention, and also for thirty six pounds six shillings Stg. as the value of coals for burning the seven hundred and twenty six tons of limestone before mentioned, at one shilling Stg. per ton, and for the sum of sixty pounds, eleven pounds eight shillings and forty pounds, all Stg. money paid by him in cash, conform to retired Bills and Receipts shown to me, The amount of all which credit is five hundred and forty three pounds seventeen shillings and fourpence Stg. leaving a balance still due by the said William Burns at Whitsunday seventeen hundred and eighty two of two hundred and thirty one pounds two shillings and eight pence Stg., which balance I Decern and Ordain the said William Burns to make payment of to the said David McClure, together with the interest thereof from the said term of Whitsunday seventeen hundred and eighty two and in time coming untill payment, and upon such payment being made to the said David McClure I Decern both Parties to discharge each other of all claims they had against each other respecting the rent or damages of the said farm of Lochlie or any other account whatever preceding the said term of Whitsunday seventeen hundred and eighty two; And I appoint this my final Decreet Arbitral to be obtempered and fulfilled by both Parties under the penalty in the said Submission, and that these presents be registered along therewith and Minutes thereon for execution, in terms of the clause of registration consented to by both Parties in the said Submission,

In Witness Whereof I have subscribed these presents, consisting of this and the three preceding pages of stamped paper written by

David McWhinnie, Clerk to Charles Shaw, Writer in Air, at Sundrum the sixteenth day of August seventeen hundred and eighty three, before these witnesses, Alexander Montgomerie, Esquire of Coilsfield, and David Shaw, Clerk to said Charles Shaw, witnesses also to my signing the marginal notes upon the second and third pages being wrote by said David McWhinnie.

Alexr. Montgomerie, Witness

John Hamilton

David Shaw, Witness

APPENDIX III

LEASE

between

PATRICK MILLER of Dalswinton

and

ROBERT BURNS

It is contracted and agreed between the parties following viz. Patrick Miller of Dalswinton Esqr on the one part, and Robert Burns late in Mossgaville in the parish of Mauchline in Ayrshire on the other part in manner and to the effect underwritten;

that is to say, the said Patrick Miller by these presents sets and in tack and assedation Lets to the said Robert Burns, his heirs and assignees whatsoever but secluding subtenants in all events, and also secluding assignees during the natural life of the said Robert Burns, but reserving to him power to assign by any deed to take effect after his death, All and Whole that part of the Lands of Elliesland lying on the south side of the river Nith in the parish of Dunscore and Sheriffdom of Dumfries, and that for the space of Four nineteen years and crops from and after his entry thereto which is hereby declared in every respect to commence at the term of Martininas next Seventeen hundred and eighty eight;

Reserving expressly from the Lands above mentioned Two acres of any part or parts thereof which the said Patrick Miller pleases, for the purpose of planting, the planting and inclosing which two acres to be at the said Patrick Miller's sole expense, and reserving also to be planted and enclosed a belt of twenty yards in breadth along the march which divides the above mentioned lands from those of Captain Riddel of the Carse, the expense of planting said belt to be defrayed by the said Patrick Miller, but the expense of inclosing the same to be disbursed by the tenant out of the three hundred pounds after mentioned.

And Reserving further for planting the Bank along the river side, the expence of planting which shall be defrayed by the said Patrick Miller. And, In respect that it is agreed upon between the said parties that the said Robert Burns shall build a dwelling house, barn, byre and stable on the said farm, on a plan to be approven of by the said Patrick Miller, and shall inclose the said lands,

For these purposes the said Patrick Miller Binds and obliges him, his heirs and successors to pay to the said Robert Burns the sum of Three hundred pounds Sterling; of which sum he is, in the course of the ensuing summer, to advance him one hundred and fifty Pounds Sterling on condition of at least building a dwelling in the course of the said summer; and to pay to him the remaining one hundred and fifty pounds afterwards in whole or in parts as the said Robert Burns shall find it necessary to receive it, upon the said Robert Burns always giving the said Patrick Miller evidence that he has expended, in carrying on the building and inclosing, sums equal to those which he shall from time to time ask and claim; and also vouching to him that he has laid out One hundred pounds of the sum first stipulated for the purposes for which he received it.

And it is also provided that, should the said Robert Burns get the building and inclosures completed for less than three hundred pounds, then the remainder of the said sums given to the said Robert Burns shall be laid out by him in the improvement of the farm as to him shall seem most expedient;

Which tack above written, with and under the reservations foresaid the said Patrick Miller binds and obliges himself and his foresaids to warrant to the said Robert Burns and his above written at all hands and against all mortals as law will.

For which causes and on the other part the said Robert Burns Binds and obliges himself and his heirs, executors and successors whomsoever to content and pay to the said Patrick Miller and his heirs or assignees the sum of Seventy pounds Sterling yearly in name of tack duty, but to be restricted for the first three years and crops to Fifty pounds Sterling yearly payable at two terms in the year Whitsunday and Martinmas by equal portions, beginning the first payment of the said tack duty at the term of Whitsunday seventeen hundred and eighty nine and the next term's payment at Martinmas thereafter for the first crop and year of his said possession, and so on thereafter during the currency of this lease, with a fifth part or more of each of the said termly payments in liquidate penalty in case of faillie and the legal interest thereof from the respective terms when the same became due and during the not payment of the same.

And further, as it is agreed by the said parties that the said Robert Burns shall be allowed to make use of the houses and pasture the grass of the said farm from Whitsunday to the said term of Martinmas next, which is above declared to be the commencement of this lease, therefore the said Robert Burns hereby Binds and obliges him and his foresaids to pay to the said Patrick Miller and his foresaids, for the said houses and grass so to be used by him, such a sum as shall at the time be agreed upon by the said parties, and, failing such agreement, then the said Robert Burns and his foresaids shall pay for the same such sum as shall be fixed upon by an Arbiter mutually chosen by the said parties. And also the said Robert Burns Binds and obliges him and his foresaids to labour and manure the lands hereby let in a proper manner during the currency of this lease; and, during the last six years thereof, not to keep more than one third of the said lands in crop each year, and during that period to use a sufficient quantity of manure with whatever crop he lays down the lands.

Moreover he binds and obliges himself and his foresaids to build and complete the aforesaid dwelling house and the other buildings and execute the inclosing on this said farm in manner above mentioned, and particularly of the belt of planting above specified, Declaring always that the enclosures to be made on said farm shall consist of Six in number, or of any other number which the said parties shall afterwards agree upon, the said Robert Burns and his foresaids being always obliged to make the said enclosures sufficient and to leave the same in that state at the ish of the lease; and which dwelling house the said Robert Burns becomes bound to finish and complete during the course of the ensuing summer. And further that he or his foresaids shall make no encroachments on the said river of Nith, by making any

Caul, pier, or embankment, throwing in stones or rubbish, or by driving piles or in any other manner of way whatever. And the said Robert Burns Binds and obliges himself and his foresaids to remove himself and his family, servants, goods and gear furth of the said lands at the expiry of this lease without any previous warning or process of removing to that effect, and leave the houses and offices in a tenantable condition at his said removal; And further, Both parties bind and oblige themselves and their foresaids to implement and perform their respective parts of the premises to each other under the penalty of One hundred pounds Sterling to be paid by the party failing to the party performing or willing to perform over and above performance, And they consent to the registration hereof in the Books of Council and Session or any other competent that letters of horning on six days charge and other necessary execution may pass on decree to be interponed hereto in form as effeirs and to that effect they Constitute their procurators &c.

IN WITNESS WHEREOF they have subscribed these presents consisting of this and the three preceding pages and likewise a duplicate hereof all written on stampt paper by Thomas Walker Baird Clerk to John Gordon Writer to the Signet at Edinburgh this eighteenth day of March One Thousand Seven Hundred and Eighty Eight years before these witnesses the said Thomas Walker Baird and John Murray one of the Clerks in the Bank of Scotland's office.

John Murray, Witness   Patrick Miller
Thos W. Baird, Witness   Robert Burns

GLOSSARY

Account of Charge and Discharge	A form of account of transactions, usually by trustees.
accused	A person charged with committing a crime or offence.
adjustments	Alterations to written **pleadings.**
advocate	A member of the **Faculty of Advocates,** a Scottish equivalent of a **barrister.**
advocate depute	A person appointed by the Lord Advocate to prosecute in the **High Court of Justiciary.**
Answers	A statement setting out the factual and legal responses to an action.
appeal	An action by a losing party taking the issue to a higher court for review.
arbiter	A person appointed to adjudicate on a dispute outwith the courts.
arrestment	Attachment by the court of money or moveable property in the hands of a third party pending the outcome of a case.

assedation	A lease of land.
Assignation	The transfer of a right.
averment	Claim or allegation.
bankruptcy	Where a person is unable to meet his debts in full, a **creditor** may apply to the court for that person's **sequestration**.
barrister	A lawyer with exclusive rights to practise in the superior courts e.g. in England.
Bill	A negotiable instrument, an order signed by the granter requiring the addressee to pay money to a third party, or to the bearer.
Bill Chamber	A vacation court at the **Court of Session**, abolished 1933.
Books of Council and Session	The Registers of Deeds kept in Edinburgh.
brutum fulmen	Something of no practical effect.

calling date	The date a case is brought before the **Sheriff**.
caution	A financial guarantee for the **expenses** of a court action or for the protection of the claim of a party to a case.
cessio bonorum	Surrender of property by a **debtor** to his/her **creditors**.
College of Justice	Created in 1532, it consisted of the **Lords of Council and Session** (the judges of the **Court of Session**) who are the **Senators of the College of Justice**, the **Faculty of Advocates**, the clerks to the Signet (later the Writers to the Signet, a society of solicitors) and the macers (the court officer who carried a mace before the judges).
Commissary	Relating to establishing succession rights in estates of deceased persons.
copyright	An intellectual property right in an original work (usually literary or artistic).

counsel	A member of the **Faculty of Advocates** in practice at the Scottish Bar.
Court of Oyer and Terminer	A commission of judges commanded to make diligent inquiry into treason.
Court of Session	The supreme civil court in Scotland. **Appeal** from it was formerly available to the House of Lords, now the Supreme Court in London.
crave	The statement of the precise order sought in the **Sheriff Court**.
creditor	A person to whom a **debtor** is due a liability.
debtor	A person obliged to fulfil an obligation – money or otherwise – to a **creditor**.
decern	To give a **decree** or judgment and authorise implementation of it.
Decree(t)	A judgment.

defamation

A statement which harms the character of another.

defences

The statement by way of response lodged by a **defender** in a civil case.

defender

A person against whom a civil action is brought.

defunct

Deceased.

de judicio sisti

A guarantee for performance of a judgment.

dilapidations

Repairs required at the end of a lease.

diligence

Generic term for methods by which a creditor may recover a debt.

Discharge

Release from an obligation.

executor(-rix)

A person named in the Will or appointed by the court, where there is no valid Will, to gather and distribute the estate of a deceased person.

exoner

To relieve from liability.

expenses
The costs of a court case that the court may order the successful party to recover from the unsuccessful party.

extract/extract decree
A written instrument signed by a clerk of court containing a statement of a **decree** or order of the court and, if necessary, a **warrant** to charge the **debtor** and to execute all competent **diligence**.

factor *loco tutoris*
Court-appointed manager of finances for a person under age.

Faculty of Advocates
A society of members of the Scots Bar.

fugitation
Fleeing from justice.

guardian
A person appointed by a parent or a court to act as the legal representative of the child in the event of the parent's death, or a person appointed by a court to act as guardian in relation to the

property, financial affairs or personal welfare of a person with incapacity.

heritable estate/property   The term for property in the form of land and houses.

heritable security   Mortgage.

High Court of Justiciary   The superior criminal court in Scotland.

in meditatione fugae   About to leave the jurisdiction of the court.

inamorata   Lover.

Inner House   The appellate division of the **Court of Session**.

insolvency   The state of **bankruptcy** – usually of an individual.

interdict   A court order preventing someone from doing something.

interim   In the meantime. A temporary court order.

liferent (or life interest)   The right of a person during his or her life to use assets or receive the income from them.

liquidation

The procedure for winding up a limited company which cannot meet its debts.

liquidator

The person appointed to collect the assets for distribution to the **creditors** of a limited company in **liquidation**.

Lord Justice Clerk

The second most senior judge in Scotland.

Lord Justice General of Scotland

The most senior criminal judge, president of the **High Court of Justiciary**.

Lord Ordinary

The title of a judge sitting in the **Outer House**.

Lord President of the Court of Session

The most senior civil judge, President of the **Court of Session** and the head of the judiciary.

Lords of Council and Session

The formal title of judges sitting in the **Court of Session**.

mandatory	A person within the jurisdiction ordered by the court to be responsible for the conduct of a case for a party who is not resident in Scotland.
Martinmas	28th November, a date for entry to and leaving from a tenanted property.
memorial	A written argument in support of a party's case.
Messengers-at-Arms	Officers whose functions include execution of civil **warrants** of the **Court of Session**.
Multiplepoinding	An action to decide the rights of competing parties to money or property in dispute, and to discharge the holder of the fund from any further liability to the claimants.
Note (or Promissary Note)	Unconditional promise to pay.
Outer House	The division of the **Court of Session** which hears cases at first instance.

oversman	Umpire where **arbiters** disagree.
Petition	A **writ** by which some civil court proceedings are started.
pleadings	Formal written presentation of a civil case.
Pleas-in-law	Short propositions at the end of a written case detailing what the proponent requires the court to do.
poinding	Impounding of moveable estate.
prescription	The rules making certain obligations unenforceable after a period of time.
prima facie	At first sight or on first consideration.
process	The court papers relating to a case.
procurator	Agent.
Procurator fiscal	The public prosecutor in the **Sheriff Court**.

pursuer	The person suing a **defender** in a civil court action.
quoad ultra	As regards everything else.
recuse	To stand down, e.g. as a judge in a case.
relict	A widow or widower in relation to succession.
renunciation	Abandonment.
respondent	(1) A person who opposes a **Petition**; or (2) A person against whom an **appeal** to a higher court is made.
Retrocession	A transfer back to the granter of an **Assignation**.
review	Reconsideration by a higher court on **appeal**.
roup	Public auction.
satrap	The governor of a province.
secluding	Excluding.

sedition (or seditious libel)   All practices whether oral or written which are intended to disturb the peace of the State for the purpose of producing insurrection.

Senator of the College of Justice   Judge of the supreme courts of Scotland.

separatim   In **pleadings**, anything apart from what has been already stated.

sequestration   To formalise the state of **bankruptcy** by court proceedings.

Sheriff   A judge in the **Sheriff Court**.

Sheriff Clerk   The clerk of court dealing with administration.

Sheriff Court   The principal inferior court.

sheriff officer   An officer of the **Sheriff Court** responsible for serving documents and executing orders made by a **Sheriff**.

sist   (1) To call a halt to proceedings in the meantime;

	or (2) To bring someone into a case as a party.
Solicitor General	The law officer assisting the **Lord Advocate**.
stat nominis umbra	(1) He/she stands under the shadow of another's name or (2) His/her real name is undisclosed.
statute	An Act of Parliament.
Style (or stile)	A form of a document used as a model.
Summons	The form of **writ** initiating certain actions in the **Court of Session.**
superiors	In feudalism, those entitled to ground rent or feu duty from owners holding a lesser interest.
Suspension	The means by which implementation of a court **decree** is put on hold.
tack	Lease.

tacksman	Tenant.
treason	The offence of making war on the Sovereign, encompassing various specific offences against the Sovereign and the State.
tutor (or *tutrix)*	The **guardian** of person under the age of capacity.
warrant	A document issued by a court authorising certain actions such as the detention of a person.
Whitsunday	28th May, a date for entry to and leaving from a tenanted property.
writ	Initiating document in a court action.
Writer to the Signet	Edinburgh lawyer with exclusive rights regarding court documents.

NOTES

Chapter 1

1. Chambers, Robert and Wallace, William, *Life and Works of Robert Burns*, Vol. 1, p. 11.
2. See Appendix I for transcription of Submission and Decree Arbitral. National Records of Scotland (NRS), RD-232-1.

Chapter 2

1. Boswell, James, *The Life of Samuel Johnson, LL.D.*, p. 367.
2. Advocates Library (AL), *Blair* v. *Douglas Heron & Co.*, 1776 Faculty Decisions, p. 223.
3. AL, *Douglas Heron & Co.* v. *Hair*, 1778 Faculty Decisions, p. 57.
4. Ibid.

Chapter 3

1. Chambers & Wallace, *Life and Works*, Vol. 1, p. 67.
2. Ibid., p. 80.

Chapter 4

1. Chambers & Wallace, *Life and Works*, Vol. 1, p. 288.
2. Robert Burns Birthplace Museum, Alloway (RBBM), Object No. 3.6013.
3. Allan Nicolson, constructed document.
4. Original held by RBBM, Object No. 3.6013.
5. See Appendix II for transcription of Decree Arbitral. NRS, SC6/70/96B.
6. Allan Nicolson, document constructed from Register of Decreets, 25th August 1783, NRS, CS/271/41553.

7. Allan Nicolson, document constructed from Register of Decreets, 27th January 1784, NRS, CS/22/653.

Chapter 5

1. Chambers & Wallace, *Life and Works*, Vol. 1, p. 111.
2. Ibid., Vol. 1, p. 107.
3. Three versions of the manuscript are held by the British Library.
4. Chambers & Wallace, *Life and Works*, Vol. 1, p. 186.
5. Ibid., Vol. 1, p. 173.
6. Ibid., Vol. 1, p. 358.
7. Ibid., Vol. 1, p. 104.

Chapter 6

1. Original held by RBBM, Object No. 3.6163. See also Chambers & Wallace, *Life and Works*, Vol. 1, p. 316.
2. Allen, Francis (ed.), *The Letters of Robert Burns*, Vol. 1, p. 54.
3. Facsimile held by RBBM, Object No. 3.8311. See also Chambers & Wallace, *Life and Works,* Vol. 1, pp. 382–3.
4. Allan Nicolson, constructed document.
5. NRS, Old Parish Registers, Mauchline (604/2), p. 278.
6. Allen, *Letters*, Vol. 1, p. 289.
7. Chambers & Wallace, *Life and Works*, Vol. 1, p. 447.
8. Original document held by National Library of Scotland (NLS), Dep. 308.
9. Allan Nicolson, constructed document.

Chapter 7

1. *Edinburgh Evening Courant*, 14th December 1786.
2. Chambers & Wallace, *Life and Works*, Vol. 3, p. 27.
3. AL, *Maxwell-Campbell* v. *Montgomery*, Session Papers, Hume Collection, 1787, Vol. 18, No. 25, Defender's Memorial, p. 3.

4. Ibid., Defender's Memorial, p. 4.
5. Ibid., Pursuer's Memorial, p. 6.
6. Chambers & Wallace, *Life and Works*, Vol. 2, p. 67.
7. Ibid., Vol. 2, p. 92.
8. Ibid., Vol. 2, p. 92.

Chapter 8
1. Chambers & Wallace, *Life and Works*, Vol. 2, p. 103.
2. Ibid., Vol. 2, p. 114.
3. Original held by RBBM, Object No. 3.6045.
4. Allan Nicolson, constructed document.
5. Hogg, J. and Motherwell, W. (eds), *The Works of Robert Burns*, Vol. 4, p. 19.
6. Original held by RBBM, Object No. 3.6044.
7. Chambers & Wallace, *Life and Works*, Vol. 2, p. 156.
8. Ibid., Vol. 2, p. 156.
9. Ibid., Vol. 2, p. 157.
10. Ibid., Vol. 2, p. 92.
11. NRS, CS96/1/180.
12. Cromek, R. H., *Reliques of Robert Burns*, p. 52.

Chapter 9
1. Chambers & Wallace, *Life and Works*, Vol. 1, p. 255.
2. NRS, Grierson MSS, GD165.
3. Original held by NLS, MS 3220, f. 3.
4. See Appendix III for a transcription of Lease. Original held by The Writers' Museum, Edinburgh Museums and Galleries.

Chapter 10
1. Published in *Ayr Observer*, October 1846.
2. Chambers & Wallace, *Life and Works*, Vol. 2, p. 63.

3. Ibid., Vol. 2, p. 68.

4. Ibid., Vol. 2, p. 330.

5. Ibid., Vol. 2, p. 329.

6. Ibid., Vol. 2, p. 270.

7. Smith, J., *Historical Sketch of Lodge St. Andrew, No.179*, p. 10.

Chapter 11

1. Chambers & Wallace, *Life and Works*, Vol. 2, p. 379.

2. Original held by the National Museum of Scotland, Edinburgh, Accession No. H.OA 156.

3. Chambers & Wallace, *Life and Works*, Vol. 3, p. 243.

4. Ibid., Vol. 3, p. 61.

5. Published in *Weekly Scotsman*, 31st October 1925.

6. Published in *Weekly Scotsman*, 31st October 1925.

7. Original held by RBBM, Object No. 3.6065.

8. Chambers & Wallace, *Life and Works*, Vol. 3, p. 102.

9. Ibid., Vol. 3, p. 106.

10. Allan Nicolson, constructed document.

11. Chambers & Wallace, *Life and Works*, Vol. 3, p. 121.

Chapter 12

1. Chambers & Wallace, *Life and Works*, Vol. 2, p. 54.

2. Ibid., Vol. 2, p. 96.

3. Ibid., Vol. 3, p. 145.

4. Ibid., Vol. 4, p. 338.

5. NRS, CS271/45960.

6. Chambers & Wallace, *Life and Works*, Vol. 3, p. 163.

7. Ibid., Vol. 4, p. 307.

8. Ibid., Vol. 3, p. 178.

9. Ibid., Vol. 3, p. 231.

10. Wallace, William (ed.), *Robert Burns and Mrs Dunlop correspondence,*

Vol. 2, p.77.

11. Chambers & Wallace, *Life and Works*, Vol. 3, p. 182.

12. Ibid., Vol. 3, p. 206.

Chapter 13

1. Chambers & Wallace, *Life and Works*, Vol. 3, p. 265.

2. Ibid., Vol. 3, p. 272.

3. Ibid., Vol. 3, p. 273.

4. Original held by The Writers' Museum, Edinburgh Museums and Galleries.

5. Chambers & Wallace, *Life and Works*, Vol. 4, p. 18.

Chapter 14

1. Allen, Francis (ed.), *The Letters of Robert Burns*, Vol. 9, p. 32.

2. Ibid., Vol. 9, p. 33.

3. Riddell, Maria, *Voyages to the Madeira, and Leeward Caribbean isles*, Preface.

4. Allen, Francis (ed.), *The Letters of Robert Burns*, Vol. 9, p. 77.

5. Original held by NLS, MS 87, pp. 73–4.

6. Chambers & Wallace, *Life and Works*, Vol. 3, p. 259.

7. Ibid., Vol. 3, p. 321.

8. Allen, Francis (ed.), *The Letters of Robert Burns*, Vol. 9, p. 108.

9. Chambers & Wallace, *Life and Works*, Vol. 3, p. 330.

10. Ibid., Vol. 2, p. 100.

Chapter 15

1. Chambers & Wallace, *Life and Works*, Vol. 3, p. 397.

2. Lovat-Fraser, James, *A Short Biography of Thomas Erskine*, p. 45.

3. Original held by RBBM, Object No. 3.6338.

4. Chambers & Wallace, *Life and Works*, Vol. 4, p. 80.

Chapter 16

1. Margarot, Maurice, *Trial of Maurice Margarot*, p. 86.

2. Gerrald, Joseph, *Trial of Joseph Gerrald*, p. 10.

3. Chambers & Wallace, *Life and Works*, Vol. 4, p. 76.

4. Ibid., Vol. 4, p. 75.

5. Ibid., Vol. 4, p. 75.

6. Ibid., Vol. 4, p. 108.

7. Ibid., Vol. 4, p. 160.

8. Ibid., Vol. 4, p. 117.

9. Ibid., Vol. 4, p. 121.

10. Downie, David, *Trial of David Downie*, p. 297.

11. Chambers & Wallace, *Life and Works*, Vol. 3, p. 332.

12. Ibid., Vol. 3, p. 333.

13. Ibid., Vol. 4, p. 147.

Chapter 17

1. Original held by RBBM, Object No. 3.6358.

2. Ibid.

3. Mays, J. C. C., *Collected Works of Samuel T Coleridge*, p. 156.

4. NRS, CS235/K/2/2.

5. Chambers & Wallace, *Life and Works*, Vol. 4, p. 133.

6. Ibid., Vol. 4, p. 133.

7. Ibid., Vol. 4, p. 207.

8. Ibid., Vol. 4, p. 198.

9. Ibid., Vol. 4, p. 203.

10. Ibid., Vol. 4, p. 205.

Chapter 18

1. Chambers & Wallace, *Life and Works*, Vol. 4, p. 251.

2. Hamilton, George, *The Telegraph; A Consolatory Epistle from Thomas Muir, Esq. of Botany Bay*, p. 1.

3. Thomson, George, *A Selection of Original Scottish Airs*, Introduction.
4. Chambers & Wallace, *Life and Works*, Vol. 4, p. 269.
5. NRS, CC5/6/18/74.

Chapter 19
1. NRS, CS97/101/5.
2. Ibid., CS215/47/6/00.
3. Ibid., CS215/47/2/00.
4. Ibid., CS215/47/4/00.
5. Original held by East Ayrshire Council, Reference Number Kimmg: BUB 0033.
6. NRS, CS97/101/15.
7. Ibid., CS97/101/15.
8. Ibid., SC/15/55/3/24.
9. Ibid., SC/15/55/3/45.
10. Allan Nicolson, constructed document.
11. AL, Acts of Sederunt 1553–1790, 18th July 1688, p. 181.

Chapter 20
1. AL, *Cadell and Davies* v. *Robertson*, 5 Paton's Appeals, 493 at 495/6.
2. AL, Session Papers, Hume Collection, 1803, Vol. 52, No. 6, Pursuer's Memorial, p. 2.
3. Ibid., p. 19.
4. Douglas, David, *Familiar Letters of Sir Walter Scott*, Vol. 2, pp. 91–3.
5. Stewart and Macgoun (Publishers), *Letters Addressed to Clarinda*, pp. iii/iv.

Chapter 21
1. Langhorne, John, *Life of Langhorne*, p. 23.
2. Morley, J., *Wordsworth Complete Poetical Works*, p. 190.
3. Grierson, William, *Apostle to Burns: the Diaries of William Grierson*, p. 238.

4. Lockhart, John Gibson, *The Life of Sir Walter Scott*, Vol. 1, p. 261.
5. Ibid., Vol. 7, p. 4.
6. Scott, Sir Walter, *Miscellaneous Prose Works*, Vol. 4, p. 394.

Chapter 22

1. Mackenzie, Peter, *Reminiscences of Glasgow and the West of Scotland*, Vol. 2, p. 333.
2. McLehose, W. C., *The Correspondence between Burns and Clarinda: with a memoir*, p. 286.
3. Ibid., p. 53.

BIBLIOGRAPHY

Allen, Francis (ed.), *The Letters of Robert Burns* (London, 1927)

Blanchard, W., *Trial of Robert Watt* (Edinburgh, 1795)

Boswell, James, *The Life of Samuel Johnson LL.D* (London, 1791)

Chambers, Robert and Wallace, William, *Life and Works of Robert Burns*, 4 vols (Edinburgh, 1896)

Cromek, R. H., *Reliques of Robert Burns* (London, 1808)

Currie, James (ed.), *The Complete Works of Robert Burns* (London, 1824)

Douglas, David, *Familiar Letters of Sir Walter Scott* (Edinburgh, 1894)

Downie, David, *Trial of David Downie, for high treason* (Edinburgh, 1795)

Gerrald, Joseph, *The Trial of Joseph Gerrald* (Edinburgh, 1794)

Grierson, William, *Apostle to Burns: The Diaries of William Grierson* (Edinburgh, 1981)

Hamilton, George, *The Telegraph; A Consolatory Epistle from Thomas Muir, Esq. of Botany Bay* (Edinburgh?, 1796)

Hogg, J. and Motherwell, W. (eds), *The Works of Robert Burns* (Glasgow, 1835)

Langhorne, John, *The Poetical Works of Langhorne* (London, 1798)

Lockhart, John Gibson, *The Life of Sir Walter Scott* (Edinburgh, 1902)

Lovat-Fraser, James, *A Short Biography of Thomas Erskine* (Cambridge, 1932)

Mackenzie, Peter, *Reminiscences of Glasgow and the West of Scotland*, 4 vols (Glasgow, 1866)

McLehose, W. C., *The Correspondence between Burns and Clarinda: with a Memoir* (Edinburgh, 1843)

Margarot, Maurice, *The Trial of Maurice Margarot* (Edinburgh, 1794)

Mays, J. C. C., *Collected Works of Samuel T Coleridge* (Princeton, 2001)

Morley, J. (ed.), *Wordsworth Complete Poetical Works* (London, 1888)

Palmer, Thomas F., *The Trial of the Rev. Thomas Fyshe Palmer* (Edinburgh, 1793)

Riddell, Maria, *Voyages to the Madeira, and Leeward Caribbean Isles* (Edinburgh, 1792)

Scott, Sir Walter, *Miscellaneous Prose Works*, 6 vols (Edinburgh, 1827)

Smith, James, *Historical Sketch of Lodge St. Andrew, No.179* (Dumfries, 1901)

Smith, James, *History of Lodge St. Michael's Kilwinning, No. 63* (Dumfries, 1895)

Smith, James, *History of the Old Lodge of Dumfries* (Dumfries, 1892)

Snyder, F. B., *The Life of Robert Burns* (New York, 1932)

Stewart & Macgoun (Publishers), *Letters Addressed to Clarinda* (Glasgow, 1802)

Thomson, George, *A Selection of Original Scottish Airs* (London, 1799)

Wallace, William (ed.), *Robert Burns and Mrs Dunlop Correspondence* (London, 1898)

Watt, Robert, *Trial of Robert Watt, for High Treason* (Edinburgh, 1795)

INDEX

Jacobitism, 4, 99, 106, 192, 201, 233, 298
Johnson, James, 77, 105, 107, 124, 154, 189, 203
Johnston, William, 197–8

Kilmarnock Edition, xi, 21, 50, 53, 60, 67, 77–8, 309
Knight, Joseph, 232

Laurie, Anna (Annie), 135
Laurie, Sir Robert, 135, 144
Lewars, John, 147, 188
Lochlie Farm, 6, 14, 17, 20, 25–36, 39–40, 55
Lorimer, Jean ('Chloris'), 223–5
Lorimer, William, 197–8

Mackenzie, Henry (Crown Agent), 75, 77–81 86–8, 91, 155, 187, 294
Maclaurin, John, 137, 156, 232, 309
Maconachie, Allan, *see* Meadowbank, Lord
Macqueen, Robert, *see* Braxfield, Lord Justice Clerk
Margarot, Maurice, 205, 212–13, 226
Maxwell, Dr William (poet's doctor), 8, 207, 208, 233, 249, 257, 270–1, 276
Maxwell-Campbell, Charles, 48, 73, 82, 84, 87, 159–60
Maxwell-Campbell, Eleanora (wife of Charles), 82, 87, 159
McAdam, John (of Craigengillan), 32–4, 69
McClure, David (of Shawwood), 6–7, 14, 25–36, 41, 111
McCraken, William, 207, 233, 241, 243, 248–52, 298
McCulloch, David, 220
McLehose, Mrs Agnes ('Clarinda'), xii, 51, 89, 106–7, 113, 127, 128, 129, 136–7, 172, 175–6, 252, 278–81, 306–310
McLehose, Andrew, WS (son of Agnes), 303, 305–10
McLehose, James (husband of Agnes), 106, 306
McLehose, William Charles (grandson of Agnes), 310
McLeod, John (of Coldbeck), 218